MW01092008

Urban Pest Management of Ants in California

John Klotz
Urban Entomology Specialist
Department of Entomology
University of California, Riverside

Laurel Hansen
Instructor
Life Science Department
Spokane Falls Community College, Washington

Herb Field
Chief Operating Officer
Lloyd Pest Control
San Diego, California

Michael Rust
Professor of Urban-Industrial Entomology
Department of Entomology
University of California, Riverside

David Oi
Research Entomologist
USDA Agricultural Research Service
Center for Medical, Agricultural, and Veterinary Entomology
Gainesville, Florida

Ken Kupfer
Environmental Pest Management Systems Developer
KM Ant Pro LLC
Nokomis, Florida

University *of* **California**
Agriculture and Natural Resources

Publication 3524

To order or obtain ANR publications and other products, visit the ANR Communication Services online catalog at http://anrcatalog.ucdavis.edu or phone 1-800-994-8849. You can also place orders by mail or FAX, or request a printed catalog of our products from

University of California
Agriculture and Natural Resources
Communication Services
1301 S. 46th Street
Building 478 - MC 3580
Richmond, CA 94804-4600
Telephone 1-800-994-8849 or 510-665-2195
FAX 510-665-3427
E-mail: danrcs@ucdavis.edu

Publication 3524

ISBN-13: 978-1-60107-664-9

Illustration and photo credit are given in the captions. The illustrations on pages i, 1, 11, 13, and 37 are from the *California Master Gardener Handbook*, ed. Dennis R. Pittenger, 2002, page 209. Cover photo by Eric Paysen; design by Celeste A. Rusconi.

To simplify information, trade names of products have been used. No endorsement of named or illustrated products is intended, nor is criticism implied of similar products that are not mentioned or illustrated.

 This publication has been anonymously peer reviewed for technical accuracy by University of California scientists and other qualified professionals. This review process was managed by the ANR Associate Editor for Urban Pest Management.

 Printed in the United States on recycled paper.

4m-pr-7/10-LR/CR

Warning on the Use of Chemicals

Pesticides are poisonous. Always read and carefully follow all precautions and safety recommendations given on the container label. Store all chemicals in the original labeled containers in a locked cabinet or shed, away from food or feeds, and out of the reach of children, unauthorized persons, pets, and livestock.

Confine chemicals to the property being treated. Avoid drift onto neighboring properties, especially gardens containing fruits or vegetables ready to be picked.

Do not place containers containing pesticide in the trash nor pour pesticides down sink or toilet. Either use the pesticide according to the label or take unwanted pesticides to a Household Hazardous Waste Collection site. Contact your county agricultural commissioner for additional information on safe container disposal and for the location of the Hazardous Waste Collection site nearest you.

Dispose of empty containers by following label directions. Never reuse or burn the containers or dispose of them in such a manner that they may contaminate water supplies or natural waterways.

CONTENTS

FIGURES

TABLES

PREFACE

In 1990 Ron Knight and Michael Rust conducted their landmark survey of urban pest ants in California. They found that throughout the state the Argentine ant was the most common urban ant pest and the most difficult to control. Since then this invasive species has continued its spread into urban, agricultural, and natural environments. As recently as 2007, Herb Field—with the help of pest management professionals (PMPs) at Lloyd Pest Control—determined that about 90 percent of urban pest ants in the greater San Diego area were Argentine ants. In 1998 a major urban infestation of another invasive species, the red imported fire ant, was discovered in Orange County. Its introduction and subsequent spread has led to costly quarantines of nurseries in Orange County and the Coachella Valley. Orange County residents passed a levee tax in 2004 to support the control and eradication of red imported fire ants. Despite the efforts to eradicate this species, red imported fire ants continue to spread throughout California.

Keeping pace with this dynamic and evolving landscape of invasive pest ants in California presents a formidable challenge to PMPs. These professionals are on the frontlines when it comes to battling these exotic ant pests, and often they are the first ones to intercept these accidental introductions (Hansen 2008). For example, the so-called *rasberry crazy ant* is named after the PMP in Texas, Tom Rasberry, who first discovered it in 2002 around Houston. Whether or not this particular species can gain a foothold and spread in California is unknown, but certainly the predominance of Argentine ants would be one of the primary obstacles it would have to overcome. The species commonly known as the *crazy ant (Paratrechina longicornis)* occurs sporadically in California, but infestations are limited in scope. In Temple City, for example, they thrive in an area of at most a few blocks, with surrounding streets apparently acting as barriers to the neighboring Argentine ant populations.

Although pervasive in California, exotic species are not the PMP's only concern. There are a number of native species in California that become major urban pests in some regions of the state. In mountain and coastal communities of Northern California, for example, where the Argentine ant is absent, another suite of pest ants predominates, represented by various species of carpenter ants, velvety tree ants, and the odorous house ant.

Developing effective control strategies for these various pest ants is an important goal; however, the use of insecticides should not be the only means. Given the general public's increasing environmental awareness, new and emerging regulatory issues with pesticide runoff into urban waterways, and the structural pest control industry's adoption of greener integrated pest management (IPM) strategies, there is a growing demand for less toxic, more target-specific, and environmentally-friendly pest control techniques.

IPM strategies for urban pest ants are the major focus of this publication, and it was written with the PMP's perspective in mind. However, successful management of ants requires close collaboration with the homeowner to implement nonchemical control strategies, so this publication will have an audience with the general public as well. The PMP needs to convey to the homeowner what IPM can do for them, why it is important, and what programs the PMP has to offer them. The PMP should view IPM from the standpoint of what it can do for the pest control industry, the environment, and the homeowner.

Urban Pest Ants of North America and Europe (Klotz et al. 2008) provides detailed diagnostic keys and descriptions of pest species in the United States and Europe. In this new publication we expand the control sections and provide more in-depth descriptions of IPM strategies for ants in general and for the major pest species in California in particular. It is our hope that this publication will serve as a useful reference for both PMPs and homeowners, and that it will foster their collaborative efforts in finding more environmentally-friendly solutions to urban ant problems.

ACKNOWLEDGMENTS

The contributions of Mary Louise Flint and Linda Ribera at the University of California Agriculture and Natural Resources (UC ANR) have been indispensable. Mary Louise Flint suggested the need for this publication and provided valuable editorial advice in the initial stages of writing, and Linda Ribera completed the project with her final expert revision of the manuscript. We were indeed fortunate to have these two high-caliber professionals working on our behalf.

CHAPTER ONE

Integrated Pest Management of Ants

Managing ants in the urban environment presents a significant challenge to both pest management professionals (PMPs) and homeowners. Nationwide, ants consistently rank at the top of household pests for the structural pest control industry. In California more than 50 percent of homeowners have attempted to control ants by applying insecticides (Flint 2003), and in Georgia 76 percent of homeowners reported treating their yards for red imported fire ants (Varlamoff et al. 2001). However, PMPs and homeowners achieve far different levels of ant control. For example, a survey of an infested neighborhood in San Bernardino, California, indicated that about 70 percent of the residents did their own ant control, 20 percent hired a PMP, and 10 percent did nothing to control ants (Field and Klotz 2008). Of the homeowners that did their own ant control, about 10 percent achieved complete or almost complete control, in contrast to the 60 percent success rate among those who ultimately hired a PMP.

A number of factors may contribute to the PMP's higher success rate, but training and superior control products are undoubtedly two of the primary reasons. Another critical factor that can often mean the difference between success and failure is the homeowner's willingness to cooperate with the PMP in implementing control measures. While it is the responsibility of

the PMP to educate the homeowner on conditions conducive to infestation and the measures needed to alleviate a problem, it is the homeowner who needs to follow through on these recommendations. Only by working together with the homeowner can the PMP expect to design and implement an effective integrated pest management (IPM) program.

IPM IN THE URBAN ENVIRONMENT

Managing urban pest ants can be difficult even for the trained professional. Control strategies are tailored to the unique biology of each species, and therefore require that the species be correctly identified. Since many of these species are small and nondescript, identification may require a PMP or entomologist to use a taxonomic key (Klotz et al. 2008) and magnification. Once the ant has been identified, the next step is to design an IPM strategy for that species.

FIGURE 1.1.

Mulch, landscaping logs, and dead trees provide ideal nesting sites for ants. *Photo:* Robert Corrigan.

FIGURE 1.2.

Electrical conduits provide entry points for ants into the structure (A) and should be sealed off (B). There may also be hidden access points under decks. *Photos:* (A) Robert Corrigan; (B) courtesy of UC IPM.

The California Department of Pesticide Regulation defines IPM as "…a pest management strategy that focuses on long-term prevention or suppression of pest problems through a combination of techniques such as monitoring for pest presence and establishing treatment threshold levels, using nonchemical practices to make the habitat less conducive to pest development, improving sanitation, and employing mechanical and physical controls. Pesticides that pose the least possible hazard and are effective in a manner that minimizes risks to people, property, and the environment, are used only after careful monitoring indicates they are needed according to pre-established guidelines and treatment thresholds." IPM utilizes all suitable pest management practices that are environmentally compatible and economically feasible to reduce the ant population to a tolerable level.

There are four general methods available for urban ant control (Klotz and Bennett 1992). The first three are nonchemical:

(1) **Habitat modification** or environmental modification alters conducive sites so that the ants can no longer nest and survive. For example, avoiding the use of wood bark mulches, correcting conditions conducive to infestation such as earth/wood contacts, and removing landscaping timbers eliminates potential nesting sites for several ant species (fig. 1.1).

(2) **Physical/mechanical methods** include the use of traps, screens, barriers, and other mechanical devices or construction practices to prevent or exclude ants. These include repairs or physical alterations to eliminate probable sources of infestation, such as sealing or caulking gaps where electrical and water lines enter the house (fig. 1.2) and trimming back vegetation and tree branches in contact with the roof and sides of a structure (fig. 1.3).

(3) **Biological methods** include the use of other biological organisms or their byproducts to control ants. Ideally, this provides a long term and self-sustaining approach. For example, the release of decapitating flies and infectious microbial agents for red imported fire ant control has been successful in augmenting ongoing chemical control efforts. These kinds of methods may become more extensively used in the future but are currently limited in application.

(4) **Chemical methods** use a broad spectrum of insecticides, repellents, attractants, baits, and insect growth regulators for ant control. More selective and judicial use of insecticides will reduce many problems associated with overuse of insecticides (e.g., contaminating residues, psychological worries, disposal problems, pesticide runoff).

FIGURE 1.3.

Trimming trees and shrubs away from structures should be part of a PMP's service or recommendations. *Photo:* John Klotz.

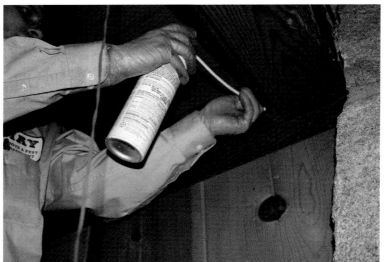

FIGURE 1.4.

Injecting nonrepellent foams, silica compounds, or a pyrethroid dust into points of access to ant nests can be an effective control measure. *Photo:* John Klotz.

FIGURE 1.5.

A thorough inspection is necessary to discover where the ants are entering a structure. *Photo:* Ken Kupfer.

Preventative measures may include the application of desiccant dusts or borates to wall voids to eliminate potential nesting sites (fig. 1.4). In California, there are around 2,200 registered pesticide products for ant control. (To access these products by active ingredient, go to "Search for Products by Chemical" at the California Department of Pesticide Regulation Web site, www.cdpr.ca.gov).

IPM AND THE HOMEOWNER

Many homeowners and PMPs mistakenly believe that IPM is a control program that does not include pesticides. The concept of IPM, however, encompasses a broad approach to ant control, which considers the biology of the target pest as well as environmental conditions in order to design a program that *minimizes* the use of pesticides.

PMPs should consider the following questions when designing an IPM program and communicate them to the homeowner:

- What is the pest species? Correct identification will provide the best control outcome, because by identifying the ant, the most effective control program based on its biology can be designed.

- What are the ants feeding on? If the ant is feeding on honeydew, which is produced by plant-sucking insects, controlling these pests might also be helpful.

- How are the ants getting into the home? There are many ways that ants get into a structure, and spending a few minutes to discover and seal or plug entry points (fig. 1.5) may reduce pesticide use or in some cases eliminate its use altogether. Inspect for tree branches touching the structure where ants can gain access, and prune them so that there is no longer contact with the structure. Caulk or seal holes where cable lines or water faucets enter exterior walls. Scout ants may trail along these structural elements into the house, searching for food or shelter. Once a resource is located, other ants will be recruited.

FIGURE 1.6.

Trash receptacles attract foraging ants, so they should be moved away from the structure. *Photo: Charles Wahl.*

FIGURE 1.7.

Buildup of leaves or pine needles on roofs or in gutters creates nest or harborage sites for various pest ants such as odorous house ants, acrobat ants, carpenter ants, and velvety tree ants. *Photo: John Klotz.*

- What other changes might be suggested around the house to reduce pest ants from colonizing nearby and prevent them from entering the home? For example, water is a critical resource for many ant species, so water conservation practices (e.g., repairing leaks) that reduce sources of excessive moisture can be helpful. Mulch can provide ideal nesting sites and, if possible, should not be piled directly in contact with the structure. Additionally, reducing or redirecting watering can help reduce pesticide runoff into storm drains. Limiting the amount of water available to the ants will also enhance their acceptance of liquid baits. Trash receptacles often attract ants, so move them away from the house (fig. 1.6); also, removal of dead trees, stumps, landscaping timbers, or limbs can eliminate nesting sites for carpenter ants and velvety tree ants.

Implementing even one of these measures can be helpful, but implementing several is better and may help reduce the amount of pesticides applied.

DESIGNING AN IPM PROGRAM

Once the pest has been identified and the extent of the infestation determined, an IPM program can be designed. A primary consideration in any ant control program is preventing the ants from getting into the structure, as most homeowners are not alarmed until ants appear inside. Consider what physical or cultural changes may be recommended to the property owner as part of an overall control strategy to eliminate the problem. It would be ideal to link the completion of the noninsecticidal approaches that you expect the property owner to perform to the guarantee on your contract. Examples of the property owner's responsibilities include

- moving firewood away from the structure
- removing debris such as leaves and pine needles from the roof or gutters (fig. 1.7)
- removing dead trees, stumps, landscaping timbers, or branches
- reducing overwatering by switching to drip irrigation and changing irrigation schedule
- removing pet foods after feeding
- caulking holes and cracks around window frames and cable lines, and weather-stripping doors

FIGURE 1.8.
To protect hummingbird feeders from ants, cut a 2-inch square piece from a sponge and make a hole in its center. Apply an over-the-counter pyrethroid spray, such as bifenthrin or permethrin, until the sponge is completely moistened. After the sponge dries, thread the suspension line through the sponge (A) so that it is located at the top of the line (B). *Photos:* Michael Rust.

FIGURE 1.9.
Cracks in concrete provide ideal nesting sites for ants; however, these areas must be treated carefully to avoid any insecticide runoff. *Photo:* Ken Kupfer.

- cutting trees and shrubs away from the structure
- removing fallen fruit on a regular basis
- moving garbage containers away from the structure and maintaining regular disposal
- protecting hummingbird feeders so that they cannot be used as a food source by ants (fig. 1.8)
- cleaning barbecue grills
- removing pet droppings

The above list is by no means all-inclusive, but it emphasizes that the property owner should be a partner in solving the ant problem. The pest control contract should include a diagram that designates the location of the problems that need to be addressed by the homeowner. Once these modifications have been communicated to the property owner, the next step is to decide if insecticides are necessary and how they will be applied. A very limited application may be all that is needed if the homeowner makes the recommended changes.

PESTICIDES AND ANT CONTROL

The potential risks of a pesticide application should always be considered beforehand. Sensitive areas include

- vegetables, fruits, spices, herbs, and other home garden foods
- children's toys and play equipment
- pet food and water dishes
- swimming pools and decorative ponds
- driveways, sidewalks, and street curbs that may contribute to insecticide runoff into storm drains (fig. 1.9)

The potential runoff of insecticides by irrigation and rainfall into urban waterways as a result of perimeter ant treatments has become a major environmental concern. PMPs need to inspect each residence for potential water runoff conditions such as drains, sprinklers near driveways and sidewalks, sloped landscape in the front yard, and driveways. Those hard surfaces likely to contribute to water runoff should

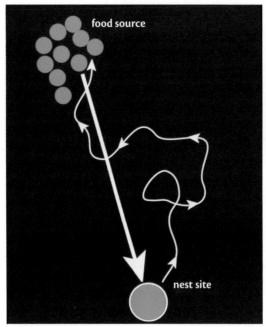

FIGURE 1.10.

A meandering search path of a scout ant followed by the shortcut back to the nest after it found food. *Photo:* John Klotz.

not be treated with liquid sprays or granules. The levels of fipronil and bifenthrin were nearly nondetectable after an experimental pin-stream application around residences. A backpack sprayer was used to apply the insecticides with the nozzle tip rotated to produce a solid stream of spray (Greenberg et al. 2010). Alternative application techniques, formulations, and strategies may greatly reduce potential insecticide runoff. We must do a better job at preventing insecticides from entering our urban waterways.

When insecticides are used, the PMP must consider the weather and the substrate to be treated, as these factors will significantly influence efficacy (Rust et al. 1996). Extreme temperatures and pH (acidity or alkalinity) of the water or the substrate to be treated can play havoc on insecticides, so it is important to know what products are most affected by heat and cold as well as alkaline and acidic conditions. The type of substrate can also affect the residual activity of an insecticide. For example, some products are neutralized when applied to concrete and others get readily absorbed into porous surfaces such as unpainted wood or mulch, thereby removing the active ingredient.

INSECTICIDE FORMULATIONS

Typically, insecticide applications for ants include baits, dusts, residual sprays, or granular treatments. Baits and dusts are often better alternatives for indoor treatments than are sprays. Baits are pesticides mixed with attractants such as food. Foraging ants bring them back to the colony (fig. 1.10). Foraging begins with scout ants leaving the nest on a meandering path in search of food. Once food is located, the scout collects or consumes some of it, depending on whether it is a solid or liquid, and then heads straight back to the nest. On its way back to the nest, the scout leaves a trail by depositing a chemical odor, or *pheromone*. Inside the nest the scout shares the food with its nest mates, stimulating them in turn to leave the nest and follow the scout's pheromone trail back to the source. As long as food is available, homeward-bound ants will continue to reinforce the trail and recruit additional workers.

Some ant baits consisting of defatted corn grits and soybean oil (with the active ingredients of hydramethylnon, pyriproxifen, or methoprene) are formulated for particular species such as fire ants or harvester ants. Other ant baits are sweet liquids, often containing disodium octaborate tetrahydrate or sodium tetraborate decahydrate, and are formulated to kill Argentine and odorous house ants. It is especially important that the bait does not kill the ants quickly so that they can carry it back to the nest. It is important that the PMP educate the homeowner about the need to allow ants to feed on the baits; likewise, homeowners should be taught to avoid applying any contact insecticides or disturbing the baits.

Baiting has become more popular in the past few years and can be an effective way to control some ant species. For example, a Pharaoh ant infestation inside a structure can usually be controlled using baits, thereby reducing any insecticide exposure to the occupants (Oi 2008). Outside baiting using gel or liquid baits can also be effective, but it is time consuming and labor intensive. Both crack-and-crevice and bait station applications of gel bait (thiamethoxam) have been very effective in reducing odorous house ant populations on

FIGURE 1.11.

Treatments with nonrepellant insecticides along the foundation and around windows and doorframes can greatly reduce foraging activity and entry of ants into structures. *Photo:* John Klotz.

FIGURE 1.12.

Outdoor perimeter sprays with fipronil applied to foundations must extend one foot up (A) and one foot out (B). *Photos:* Charles Wahl.

and near structures (K. Vail, pers. comm., 2008). Most of the liquid baits contain sugar water as the attractant and a low concentration of toxicant. It may take weeks or months before total control is achieved. Therefore, it is critical to maintain a sufficient quantity of bait in the stations at all times or the ants will go elsewhere for food. Again, it is essential for the PMP to transmit this information to the homeowner. Furthermore, where there is standing water or areas that are overwatered due to poorly managed irrigation systems, some ant species, especially Argentine ants, will use these alternate sources of water as a resource, thereby reducing their consumption of liquid bait.

Dusts containing boric acid, disodium octaborate tetrahydrate, or dessicants (diatomaceous earth or silica gel) can be applied in exterior wall voids and attic spaces to prevent ants from moving into a structure, and they will remain active for years if kept dry (Hansen and Klotz 2005). In addition, dusts placed in a wall void minimize human exposure.

Interior spray treatments for most ant species are usually not necessary. However, PMPs can use chlorfenapyr indoors. Chlorfenapyr inside and fipronil outside have been very effective in reducing indoor and outdoor odorous house ant activity (K. Vail, pers. comm., 2008). The use of pyrethroids on either the exterior or interior of a structure for ant control is no longer recommended, due to the trapping effect of these products (Rust et al. 1996). The ants are rapidly killed by such barriers and may end up trapped inside the house, creating even more problems. Spot applications of pyrethroid sprays around entry points and along trails will prevent entry for several days, but typically they must be repeatedly applied.

For exterior applications, a nonrepellent insecticide such as fipronil is highly effective as a spot (fig. 1.11) and perimeter spray (fig. 1.12) on and around the structure. The delayed action and horizontal transfer of the active ingredient promotes a thorough distribution of toxicant into the ant colony (Soeprono and Rust 2004a,b). This limited application, however, is not a stand-alone treatment,

FIGURE 1.13.

In heavy ground cover (A), a granular application (B) is more effective than spray because granules will sift down to the soil where ants are nesting or trailing. *Photos:* Charles Wahl.

and it is recommended that problem areas outside the fipronil zone be treated with other products such as baits and granular insecticides.

Certain formulations may also work better than others, depending on the microhabitat being treated. For example, a spray on heavy ground cover or mulch is ineffective because the insecticide does not penetrate to the ground where the ants may be nesting or trailing. In this case, a granular formulation is a better choice (fig. 1.13). Depending on the various microhabitats to be treated, several different formulations might be used on the same property. PMPs should always check with the manufacturer and the label before applying any product to determine its limitations.

MORE EFFECTIVE PEST MANAGEMENT

Ant control has changed dramatically over the years, and it will continue to evolve. In the past, insecticide sprays would have been applied with a power sprayer, but studies have shown that it is more effective to direct the product on ant nests and trails (Klotz et al. 2007). Furthermore, directed treatments with a backpack sprayer greatly reduce the potential of insecticide runoff into storm drains during irrigation and rainy weather. The PMP and homeowner need to ask themselves: where is water most likely to run off from the property? The homeowner needs to reduce this runoff as much as possible and PMPs should avoid spraying these areas. Water quality issues are becoming increasingly important and they will likely lead to further insecticide and treatment restrictions in the near future.

Low-toxicity baits have been proposed as an environmentally green approach to ant pest control in recent years. Some baits are formulated as a paste or gel, and enclosed within small plastic bait stations to prevent them from drying out. These products are typically used indoors where ant intrusions are limited to a few foragers, and where pesticide exposure should be minimized. Using these products outside will usually fail because the ant populations are so large that only a small portion will be affected. In addition, some ants such as Argentine ants do not prefer gels or pastes and these containerized baits are quickly rendered ineffective outside, especially during the hot, dry summer months, because they dry out.

Some liquid-bait delivery systems, however, have been designed for outside application with sufficient capacity to feed large ant populations. Normally these liquid baits are formulated with sugar as a highly preferred food and boric acid as a toxicant. Many ant species, including the Argentine ant and odorous house ant, are attracted to these sweetened liquid baits and, as a result of their use, significant reductions in numbers have been reported (fig. 1.14).

Even more effective than residual sprays of fipronil or bifenthrin was an experimental liquid bait formulated with thiamethoxam (0.003%) as the toxicant, which reduced Argentine ant numbers near the house by

FIGURE 1.14.

Liquid bait stations containing a toxicant mixed with water and sugars are effective at reducing large populations of ants outside a structure.
Photo: John Klotz.

84 percent and in the yard by 80 percent, after only two months (Klotz et al. 2009). Given the ultra-low dose of toxicant plus its point source application, achieving this level of control around homes represents a significant breakthrough in controlling Argentine ants with liquid baits. Although currently not registered for commercial use, formulations with new active ingredients such as thiamethoxam are under development.

SELLING THE CONCEPT OF IPM AND BAITING

The objective of any urban IPM program is to protect human health and property from pests by using techniques that are not environmentally disruptive, yet are effective and economical. In this regard, there is no other method of control that is more ideally suited for pest ants than using low-toxicity liquid baits. The social behavior, foraging strategies, and even internal morphology of ants can all be exploited by liquid baits to deliver and spread a toxicant throughout the entire colony. The implementation of exterior liquid-bait monitoring and delivery programs also serves to reengage the PMP with a considerable number of consumers, governmental agencies, and businesses that desire a less invasive pest management option.

Developing effective liquid ant baits presents a formidable research challenge, but

an even greater hurdle is implementing their use in the pest control industry. Two major drawbacks to their adoption are the perceived labor-intensiveness (cost-prohibitiveness) and the liability of leaving bait stations around structures. In a cost comparison of a baiting treatment and a conventional fipronil spray treatment for Argentine ants, our research showed that in order to offset the additional cost of baiting, a company would need to charge up to 40 percent more for the initial service to compensate for the installation and maintenance of bait dispensers (Klotz et al. 2009). It should be noted that during research trials the initial setup costs for baiting were higher than expected due to the thorough inspection and mapping of each property. These additional costs would likely be reduced as the PMP gains more experience with the baiting program, resulting in a further decrease in costs (Klotz et al. 2009).

The question now being posed, as more PMPs employ and modify their own baiting programs as part of their offered services, is: to what extent will baits and baiting strategies evolve in the foreseeable future? Advances in baiting technology and application techniques may well reduce costs even further. In addition, growing environmental concerns about broadcast applications of insecticides and increasing regulations to prevent pesticide runoff in urban waterways could make baiting a more competitive and attractive option in future marketplaces.

PMPs must view IPM and baiting in particular from the standpoint of what it can do for the pest control industry, their customers, and the environment. We need to take all the tools of our profession and implement them into a systematic or holistic program that is marketable. If each program is properly designed, it can be sold, and it will be effective even if it means billing the customer for this extra service. In this manner, it provides a viable competitive tool to reach consumers who are environmentally conscious and willing to pay for the extra service.

CONCLUSION

Identifying the ant pest should always be the first step in developing an IPM strategy. However, identifying ants can be difficult even for the seasoned professional. As aids to identification, taxonomic keys for urban pest ants are available (Klotz et al. 2008), and close-up color images can be accessed at the AntWeb Web site (http://www.antweb.org/). An online key for major household ants in California can also be found at the UC IPM Web site, http://www.ipm.ucdavis.edu/TOOLS/ANTKEY/. (See appendix B.)

Once the pest has been identified, a control strategy can then be designed. There are three general methods currently being used to control ants (Oi 2008):

- physical exclusion
- application of residual contact insecticides
- distribution of insecticidal baits

Physical exclusion techniques include repairs or physical alterations to eliminate probable sources of infestation, such as sealing or caulking gaps where electrical and water lines enter buildings and trimming back vegetation and tree branches in contact with the roof and sides of a structure.

Residual insecticides include spray, dust, and granular formulations that kill on contact. Broadcast applications of pyrethoid sprays and granules were once considered to act as a repellent barrier but recent research suggests that these fast-acting insecticides actually prevent ants from establishing trails across treated barriers (Soeprono and Rust 2004a).

Applications of nonrepellent insecticides such as fipronil and chlorpfenapyr do not prevent ants from establishing trails and, in fact, exploit this behavior to spread the toxicant. In addition, fipronil exhibits horizontal transfer to nestmates (Soeprono and Rust 2004b).

Baits are considered ideal for ant control because they exploit the foraging behavior and social interactions of ants. Identifying the pest ant species and selecting the correct bait are essential if baiting programs are to be successful.

In summary, an effective pest management program integrates habitat modification—as well as physical/mechanical, biological, and chemical methods—along with a thorough inspection. Long-term control will depend on the homeowner being adequately educated by the PMP on key points, such as conditions conducive to infestation, biology of specific ant species, and the importance of inspection. The PMP needs to educate the homeowner concerning the signs of infestation as an early warning of impending problems and what corrections are necessary in the form of repairs and physical alterations to eliminate probable sources of infestation. By combining inspection, education, consultation, sanitation, exclusion, habitat modification, selective use of insecticidal products, and monitoring, a more effective, longer-term pest management program can be achieved.

CHAPTER TWO

PMP Surveys of Urban Ant Pests in California and Other States

Surveys conducted by the authors show significant regional differences in species of structural pest ants (table 1.1). The varied climate of California supports a different complex of pest species from that found in the arid desert environment of Arizona and the humid tropical and subtropical climates of Florida.

CALIFORNIA

Of the approximately 281 species of ants in California (Ward 2005), a few dozen are found associated with human structures. Twenty-two species are not native. The most economically important pest species are Argentine ants and red imported fire ants, which originated in South America and were inadvertently introduced into the United States when they were offloaded with cargo or ballast from ships docking in southern ports. Once established, these invasive species then spread aggressively into the surrounding environment, out-competing and displacing native ant species. Interstate travel and trade have facilitated their transfer to other locations so that currently these ants can be found in various locations from coast to coast. Argentine ants were first detected in California in the early 1900s. Urban infestations of the red imported fire ant, however, were not detected in California until 1998 in Orange County, several years after the survey below was completed (fig. 2.1).

Table 1.1. Surveys of urban pest ants and their frequencies based on collections made by PMPs in California, Arizona, and Florida

TYPE OF ANT	CA* (%)	AZ (%)	FL (%)
leaf-cutting ants	0	13	0
carpenter ants	9.5	1.3	23
acrobat ants	1.3	0	1.3
pyramid ants	0.7	10.8	2.1
Forelius	1.3	15.9	0
field ants	4.9	0.6	0
Argentine ants	25.9	0	1.2
Pharaoh ants	4.9	0	11
crazy ants	2	3.4	18.3
big-headed ants	3.6	1.9	10.4
harvester ants	4.6	20	1.2
red imported fire ants	0*	0.6	14
southern fire ants	19.3	21.7	0
odorous house ants	11.1	7	0
ghost ants	0	0	14
pavement ants	1	0	0
other species	9.9	3.8	3.5

Source: Knight and Rust 1990 (CA); Field et al. 2007 (AZ); and Klotz et al. 1995 (FL).
Note: *Survey conducted before the red imported fire ant was found established in California in 1998.

The primary urban pest in California is the Argentine ant. Its incidence, however, varies widely across the state's diverse landscape. It makes up 85 percent of the ants collected by PMPs in the Greater San Diego Area (Field et al. 2007) compared with 41.5 percent in the San Francisco and Monterey Bay Area (Knight and Rust 1990) and none in the San Bernardino Mountain communities.

ARIZONA

The key pests collected by PMPs in Phoenix and Tucson were native species that included southern fire ants, harvester ants, leaf-cutting ants, and *Forelius pruinosus*. These ants are commonly found in hot, arid environments. The leaf-cutting ant, *Acromyrmex versicolor*, generally nests in sandy regions, and *F. pruinosus* has a high temperature tolerance. PMPs have adapted their management strategies to accommodate these desert species. Baits, for example, are commonly used to control harvester ants and southern fire ants because of some very effective formulations that are available for these species.

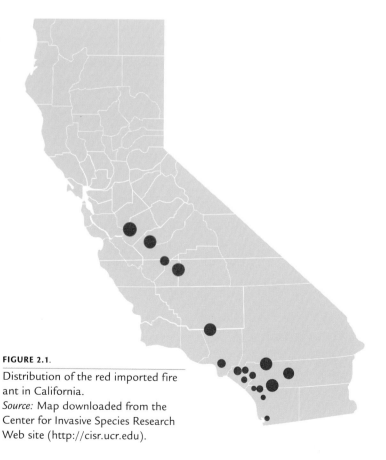

FIGURE 2.1.
Distribution of the red imported fire ant in California.
Source: Map downloaded from the Center for Invasive Species Research Web site (http://cisr.ucr.edu).

FLORIDA

Deyrup et al. (2000) reported 207 species of ants in Florida, 52 of which are exotic. The most common species collected by PMPs were the red imported fire ant, ghost ant, crazy ant, Florida carpenter ant, and Pharaoh ant. The Pharaoh ant is primarily a pest in hospitals, bakeries, factories, offices, and large domestic apartment blocks (Edwards 1986), but on occasion it shows up in households. Except for the Florida carpenter ant, these are tramp or invasive species that thrive in humid, tropical, and subtropical climates.

CONCLUSION

These surveys represent only snapshots in time of urban pest ants whose species makeup and their incidence is ever changing. For example, in Florida the pest status of the white-footed ant, *Technomyrmex difficilis*, and the big-headed ant, *Pheidole megacephala*, has significantly increased since our 1995 survey (Warner and Scheffrahn 2007). The number of exotic ant species established in the United States is staggering and continues to rise. For example, 52 of the 207 species in Florida (25%) are exotic (Deyrup et al. 2000), as are 22 of the 281 species (8%) in California (Ward 2005).

The next chapter covers in detail the biology and control of the major urban pest ants in California. The exotic species make up a substantial portion of this discussion, considering the prevalence of Argentine ants and the potential economic impact of imported fire ants. The native wood-destroying ants (carpenter ants and velvety tree ants) and odorous house ants are also covered in detail because of their frequency in the PMP ant survey described above and their overall importance to structural pest control in California and the United States.

The last chapter covers the occasional and emerging urban pest ants of California. Even though they are not as frequent or economically important as the ants covered in the previous chapter, these ants do sometimes become a nuisance to homeowners and in the case of newly introduced species have the potential of becoming established and spreading in California.

CHAPTER THREE

Major Urban Ant Pests of California

ARGENTINE ANTS

PEST STATUS

For most homeowners in the United States, the appearance of ants is just another sign of spring and warm weather; but for an increasing number of people, ant invasions have become a year-round problem. In San Francisco, for example, many residents note an increase of structural invasions by the small brown Argentine ant (fig. 3.1), which appears to be triggered by the decline of hemipterans (plant-sucking insects such as aphids, mealybugs, and scales) in August, and also in fall when the first substantial rains occur (Gordon et al. 2001). In Southern California, invasions usually begin in early June and end by late summer, with interior infestations associated with higher temperature and lack of rain, as well as reduced hemipteran populations (Rust et al. 1996).

The Argentine ant, *Linepithema humile*, is an invasive species thought to have been introduced into the United States in the late 1800s into the Port of New Orleans, most likely offloaded with cargo from Brazilian coffee ships (Newell and Barber 1913). These ants subsequently spread rapidly in the Southeast, facilitated by the railroad. Along the West Coast, they were first reported in the early 1900s in the San Francisco Bay area, subsequently spreading southward. Pockets of Argentine ants have also been reported in cities along the Interstate 5 freeway (Portland, Oregon; Seattle, Washington; and

FIGURE 3.1.

Argentine ants, *Linepithema humile*, drinking sugar water. *Photo:* Reiner Pospischil.

Vancouver, British Columbia), suggesting that commerce may be spreading them. These smaller populations appear to be established, because they invade structures on an annual basis, but they may be limited by the colder climates.

Currently the Argentine ant is the number one urban pest in California, and it is also a major pest in agriculture and natural settings (Vega and Rust 2001). In agriculture, they tend hemipteran pests for honeydew, a sugar-rich fluid that is the main component of the ants' diet. The ants protect the hemipterans from their predators and parasites, thereby interfering with the natural biological control of these pests. The excreted honeydew also damages crops, such as citrus and grapes, due to the unsightly black, sooty mold that grows on honeydew. Argentine ants can also become pests in native natural ecosystems, where by sheer numbers of individuals they out-compete and displace other native ant species. In Torrey Pines State Park in San Diego, for example, they are displacing the native harvester ant, which has a negative impact on the horned lizard population because harvester ants are the lizard's main source of food (Suarez et al. 2000).

It is in the urban environment, however, that homeowners feel the full force of Argentine ants and their tremendous populations. Their colonies around homes can reach astronomical numbers, e.g., more than a half million ant visits to bait stations placed around homes in Riverside over a 24-hour period (Reierson et al. 1998). In San Diego, Argentine ants make up 85 percent of the ants controlled by Lloyd Pest Control, the city's largest pest control firm (Field et al. 2007); with over 35,000 general pest accounts, Argentine ant control makes up the major portion of their business. About 90 percent of these infestations are located outside along sidewalks and driveways, and in and around gardens and foliage (Field et al. 2007).

Argentine ants have been reported in most of the southeastern states, but their distribution is more sporadic. For example, in Louisiana, they have been reported in isolated areas such as the Toledo Bend region, New Orleans, Baton Rouge, Shreveport, and Hammond. In North Carolina, Argentine ants were found in greater than 20 percent of the samples provided by PMPs (Bambara et al. 2008). Infestations have well-defined boundaries, such as a neighborhood, business park, or college campus (Silverman and Brightwell 2008).

IDENTIFICATION AND BIOLOGY

Argentine ant workers are small (2 to 3 mm long), brown ants, with one node, 12-segmented antennae, and a distinct bulge on the propodeum (the first abdominal segment fused to the thorax). (For equivalents between U.S. and metric systems of measurement, a conversion table is provided at the end of this publication.)

They cannot sting and rarely bite but do emit a musty odor when crushed. Queens are about twice the size of workers and perform other duties besides egg laying, such as foraging and caring for young.

Argentine ants undergo a complete metamorphosis with an egg stage, four larval instars, pupa, and adult, the entire cycle taking 78 days on average. Adult workers normally live about 10 to 12 months but queens may live for several years (Newell and Barber 1913). Winged adult males appear in the colony in spring and will go on mating flights. After flights, the workers capture and return the males to nests where mating occurs. Winged females do not fly and remain in the nest where mating occurs. Colony numbers increase by budding, in which one or more of the many queens in the parent colony leave the nest along with some workers and brood to form a new colony.

Argentine ants are unicolonial, i.e., there is no clear delineation between a colony and population, with a free flow of workers between nests. They are polygynous, meaning that a colony has many queens, on average about 15 for every 1,000 workers (Aron 2001). Thus, they have a very high reproductive potential. They forage over long distances (at least several hundred feet), so infestations are not localized to a single home but rather cover entire neighborhoods (Vega and Rust 2003). Achieving control is difficult because of their large, diffuse colonies and area-wide infestations. It has been suggested that treatments should be applied in much larger areas in order to encompass their expansive foraging territory (Vega and Rust 2003; Silverman and Brightwell 2008).

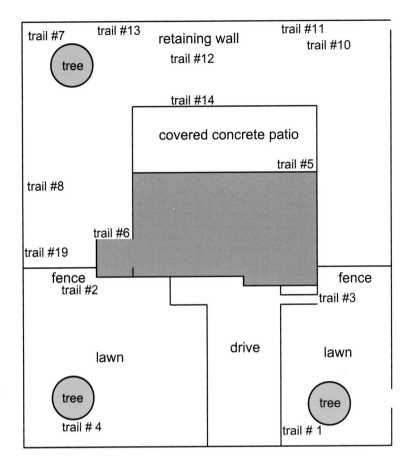

FIGURE 3.2.

Inspection diagram indicating areas of Argentine ant activity around a house. *Photo:* Michael Rust.

MANAGEMENT

Pest management of Argentine ants in agriculture has a long history dating back to the early 20th century. Over the years, a number of different control strategies have been tried, primarily using sprays and baits (Klotz et al. 2008). Perimeter sprays have been the traditional treatment strategy for controlling Argentine ants around homes; however, complete barriers are difficult to achieve because any small gaps provide access for the ants (Klotz et al. 1997). In addition, chemical degradation, irrigation, dense ground cover, mulch, high temperature, substrate alkalinity, and direct sunlight compromise the efficacy of barriers (Rust et al. 1996).

Baits have been a common approach, but unfortunately many of the commercial baits available are not palatable to Argentine ants, and those that are kill the ants before the toxicant can be dispersed through the colony (Rust et al. 2002). At best, these efforts in the past have achieved limited success. Recently significant progress has been made in the development of liquid baits for Argentine ants. However, these new formulations require special delivery systems and new application methods.

Property Inspection. A thorough inspection of the house and yard is the first step in developing an effective control program for Argentine ants. Creating a simple diagram of the property is helpful for recording areas of ant activity and determining where to place bait stations, what areas to treat with sprays and granules, and where possible nest sites are located (fig. 3.2).

Initially, a thorough inspection of the residence should be conducted—inside and out—to identify current and potential problem areas that may be conducive to ant infestations.

Inside, start at the front entrance and, using a flashlight, systematically inspect around the entire house, focusing on baseboards and walls where they meet the floor and ceiling, because ants often trail along these edges and other structural guidelines. Argentine ants will enter through cracks in the concrete slab and go unnoticed underneath the carpet (fig. 3.3). Also, inspect electrical outlets, vents, fixtures, and around and under furnishings for ant activity (fig. 3.4.). In the kitchen, bathrooms, and laundry where there are sources of water, open cabinets to inspect pipes and drains. Argentine ants evolved in moist habitats and are susceptible to desiccation, so water is an important limiting factor for their survival.

Outside, inspect as much of the structure, both high and low, as possible. If ant activity is found inside, inspect outside in the same areas for potential entry points. In some cases caulking or sealants may be sufficient to prevent their entry. Inspect the yard, noting any signs of ant activity and paying particular

FIGURE 3.3.

Argentine ants underneath a carpet. *Photo:* Michael Rust.

- sealing up potential entryways with caulk or sealant
- trimming back or removing plants that harbor ants
- moving trash receptacles away from the structure
- removing pet food dishes and cleaning around outside cooking areas that provide attractive food sources
- picking up rotting fruit
- removing debris such as leaves and pine needles from the roof or gutters

Another potential problem is excessive watering or leaky irrigation systems. For example, reducing the availability of water to the ants would facilitate a more effective baiting program. Therefore, the homeowner should make the needed repairs or schedule fewer watering days during the week with longer duration in order to maintain the attraction of liquid baits to the ants.

Baiting. A wide variety of solid, gel, and liquid baits is being sold for ant control. However, it is extremely important to use only baits that are effective against a particular species. Baits are often too toxic, killing ants before they can recruit nestmates. Sweet liquid baits are ideal control measures for Argentine ants because they exploit their biology and social behavior. Over millions of years, ants coevolved with plant-piercing and sucking insects such as aphids, mealybugs, and scales, and they have developed specialized digestive tracts and recruitment behaviors to collect and share honeydew (Hölldobler and Wilson 1990). Sweet liquid baits capitalize on this mutual association as long as the toxicant is at a low enough concentration that it does not interfere with trophallaxis (oral exchange of food) and recruitment (Rust et al. 2004).

Low-toxicity liquid baits have three distinct advantages: (1) they are target-specific, thus minimizing collateral damage to beneficial insects; (2) they capitalize on the recruitment and food-sharing behavior of ants, whereby scout ants recruit their nest mates to newly discovered food, and these recruited ants return to the nest to share the food with the rest of the colony; and (3) they are not broadcast in the environment, reducing environmental impact (insecticide runoff into urban waterways). A major disadvantage of

attention to trees, shrubs, and potted plants which might harbor plant-sucking insects, such as aphids, mealybugs, and scales, or potential nesting sites for ants. Use a screwdriver or probe to move mulch, small concrete pavers, and soil in potted plants. Additionally, move potted plants as colonies will often become established in the soil and are not noticeable until the pot is moved.

As Argentine ants are constantly seeking new sources of food and water, keep in mind that infestations often progress onto a property from surrounding areas. Note the location of nests. A screwdriver can be used to tap utility boxes and probe the soil in potential 'hot spots' such as around trees and shrubs and other moist, shaded areas. Argentine ants also will nest in leaf litter, mulch, under rocks and other objects, and sometimes within the structure or under the foundation. Although full sun exposure and brightly illuminated surfaces are not conducive to ant activity, at other times of the day these same areas may be teeming with ants. To avoid this problem, conduct inspections in the early morning or late afternoon.

Nonchemical Control Measures. The PMP should educate the customer on what corrections are necessary in the form of repairs, physical alterations, and sanitary measures to eliminate probable sources of infestation:

FIGURE 3.4.

Dead Argentine ants in a freezer compartment showing their location (A) and a close-up (B). *Photos:* Michael Rust.

liquid baiting programs is that they are labor-intensive to install and maintain, making them less cost-effective than more traditional treatments.

It is important to remember that only a small percentage of an ant colony forages (some estimate it to be near 10 percent). Argentine ants will forage 24 hours a day when temperatures range from about 50° to 95°F (10° to 35°C), and their trails may consist of thousands of ants traveling to and from nests. Research has shown that Argentine ants can forage at least 200 feet away from their nest (Vega and Rust 2003).

Bait Stations. Some important features to look for when selecting a liquid bait station for Argentine ants include the following:

- sufficient volume of sugar water-based liquid bait
- constant bait formulation, i.e., little to no evaporation
- no dead ants accumulating in the bait
- easy to refill and relocate
- inexpensive

Large reservoirs of bait are necessary because Argentine ant populations can consume 16 ounces of bait within 2 weeks and it is important to maximize the amount of bait consumed before foraging activity declines. Secondly, it is important that the toxicant concentrations remain at a constant level. Effective baits provide delayed toxicity and any evaporation of water can increase the speed of their toxicity. Dead ants accumulating in the bait station repel other ants and decrease the effectiveness of the bait station. Lastly, bait stations need to be easy to fill and maintain. Ideally, the baits should be inexpensive to help offset the increased labor costs of baiting.

A variety of liquid bait stations are available to PMPs. A few are listed below, along with a brief description of each:

(a) One that has been used extensively in experimental tests to evaluate liquid baits for Argentine ants is the KM AntPro (fig. 3.5). It provides ants with a 360-degree access to the feeding area, and can hold 19 ounces of bait in its reservoir, which is inaccessible to the ants

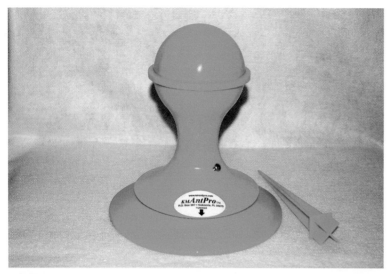

FIGURE 3.5.

KM AntPro bait dispenser. *Photo:* Ken Kupfer.

FIGURE 3.6.

Ants-No-More. *Photo:* Courtesy of UC IPM.

FIGURE 3.7.

Ant Café. *Photo:* Ken Kupfer.

so that the bait cannot be contaminated.

(b) The Ants-No-More bait station (fig. 3.6) has a 4-ounce capacity and is waterproof. The ants enter the reservoir through holes in the stake.

(c) The Ant Cafe (fig. 3.7) with 1-ounce capacity can be used indoors where it can be secured to walls, cabinets, and windowsills.

(d) The prefilled Terro-PCO Liquid Ant Bait Stations (fig. 3.8) contain 0.36 ounces of liquid bait (5.4% borax).

Liquid Baits. Depending on the active ingredient and bait formulation, the effective concentration of a toxicant varies. Experimental baits consisting of 25 percent sucrose water, 1×10^{-4} percent thiamethoxam or fipronil, and 0.5 to 1.0 percent boric acid are formulated at the appropriate concentrations to provide a delayed effect of the toxicant, thereby giving the ants time to distribute the bait throughout the colony.

Placement and Number of Bait Stations. The primary considerations in a baiting program are station placement and number of stations. Below are some guidelines to follow for successful ant control:

1) Placement of bait stations:

If the ants are invading the home or nesting in shrubs near the house, install at least one station on each side of the structure, giving consideration to the building's size and the number of connecting walls. For a small house or building (1,500 square feet), place one unit on each side. Some additional points to consider in bait placement:

- Ant traffic often converges at the junction of two walls.

- Ants are attracted to sources of water such as the overflow outlet on air conditioners and spigots for irrigation.

- Ant activity is often high on the north side of structures due to increased shade and moisture.

Ideally bait stations should be placed where ants are trailing, preferably in shrub or tree belts so as not to interfere with lawn maintenance (fig. 3.9). However, avoid locations where substantial water runoff will occur and locations with full sun exposure. Do not put bait stations directly over nests; instead, when possible, place them at least 5 feet away from

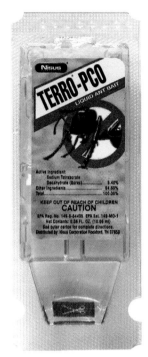

FIGURE 3.8.

Terro-PCO. *Photo:* Ron Dawson.

FIGURE 3.9.

Bait stations should be placed in areas with ant activity out of direct sunlight as shown in (A) near irrigation lines that provide guidelines for trailing ants and in (B) adjacent to walls where ants often trail. *Photos:* Ken Kupfer.

nests, allowing the ants to locate the food on their own. Do not disturb nests or spray the area with insecticide.

After one or two weeks, move the stations away from the structure when possible so that the ants are no longer attracted to the structure, which increases the probability of infestations inside the building.

2) Number of bait stations to use per home:

The number of bait stations will depend on the severity of the infestation. A good rule of thumb is to place a bait station in any area where heavy ant traffic occurs. This might be at the base of fruit trees, near garbage cans, or next to pools or ponds. Smaller infestations may be baited with higher percentage boric acid baits (5.4%), when, for example, the goal is to eliminate ants quickly from an indoor incursion. In this case a large bait station is unnecessary because the bait is fast acting and limited in exposure to a small population of ants.

When Argentine ant populations are no longer located near or inside the residence or structure, relocate the bait stations to shaded areas where they are least likely to be disturbed. This provides a continuous defense against reinfestation. Keep in mind that when existing ant populations are eliminated, other ants may eventually move into the area. Therefore, keep bait stations activated and in place, serving as sentinels to prevent reinfestation. We often refer to this as *diversionary baiting*. When the structure to be protected has minimal area surrounding the structure, leave the bait stations in place continuously.

FIGURE 3.10.

Perimeter spray applications using a backpack sprayer are effective treatments for Argentine ants. *Photo:* John Klotz.

FIGURE 3.11.

Ants frequently nest and trail along the edges of sidewalks and driveways, and care must be taken when treating these areas because of insecticide run-off. *Photo:* Charles Wahl.

Discuss the following points with the homeowner:

- Baits are slow-acting, thus requiring ants to forage and remove the bait.
- Homeowners should not disturb the bait stations or spray insecticides near them.
- Depending on the bait, it may take several days to weeks for the baits to completely control the ant infestation.

Sprays. Some very effective spray formulations for Argentine ant control are available to PMPs, which can be applied with a backpack or other type of compressed air sprayer (fig. 3.10). These include pyrethroids, such as bifenthrin, cyfluthrin, and cyhalothrin, and the nonrepellent insecticide, fipronil. Fipronil is particularly effective because it is slow acting and exhibits horizontal transfer, i.e., it spreads from one ant to another by physical contact (Soeprono and Rust 2004a,b). The foraging ants pick up the active ingredient and spread it through the colony. Pyrethroids, on the other hand, kill on contact and exhibit little horizontal transfer (Soeprono and Rust 2004b), yet are highly effective. The barriers kill foragers quickly, preventing them from establishing trails. On occasion pyrethroid barriers prevent ants from escaping the structure and thus cause a problem indoors, especially if the ants are nesting beneath the concrete slab. Additional indoor treatments may then be necessary.

In the past several years, we have been conducting experimental studies to reduce the amount of insecticide applied around homes to control Argentine ants. Applications of 1 to 4 gallons of the above-mentioned pyrethroids and fipronil at the label recommended rates reduced ant activity by 90 percent. In addition to spraying the perimeter of the house, the sprays were also directed at ant trails in the yard (fig. 3.11). The most effective treatment was a combination of a fipronil spray with a broadcast application of bifenthrin granules in foliage outside the spray zone. However, perimeter sprays with fipronil are now restricted to the structure and no more than one foot away.

Care was taken to avoid treating hard surfaces such as sidewalks, driveways, or patios with granular insecticides. Surprisingly, an experimental spot treatment with one gallon of fipronil applied only to active ant trails provided significant reductions comparable to the higher volume treatments, which illustrates the potency of this product when applied directly to the ants (Klotz et al. 2007). Spot applications to holes or cracks in the structure will also help prevent ant invasions (fig. 3.12). Ideally, these areas should be sealed and repaired to prevent future access.

FIGURE 3.12.

A spot application of insecticide to a potential entry point for ants. *Photo:* Charles Wahl.

CONCLUSION

The Argentine ant is one of the most successful urban invasive ant species. It is found on six continents and is listed among "100 of the World's Worst Invasive Species" on the Global Invasive Species Database (Lowe et al. 2000). In recent years, research has demonstrated that Argentine ant populations can be managed and greatly reduced with the implementation of a well-planned IPM program. The program includes the use of liquid baits, slow-acting sprays, fast-acting barriers, and granular treatments. To achieve this goal requires some familiarization with the Argentine ant's biology and foraging behavior.

FIRE ANTS

PEST STATUS

The red imported fire ant, *Solenopsis invicta* (fig. 3.13), is the most notorious urban ant pest due to its aggressive nature and injurious sting. The economic cost of fire ants in the United States is estimated at $6.3 billion per year (Lard et al. 2006). The majority of losses are in the urban sector, with a large portion of the costs attributed to chemical treatments,

FIGURE 3.13.

Workers of the red imported fire ant, *Solenopsis invicta* (A); southern fire ant, *Solenopsis xyloni* (B); and tropical fire ant, *Solenopsis geminata* (C). *Photos:* Sanford Porter and David Oi.

Table 3.1. Common fire ants in California and southwestern states

Scientific name	Common name	Geographic distribution	Size and color of workers
Solenopsis invicta	red imported fire ant	southern U.S., NM, CA	1.6–5 mm; almost uniformly dark reddish brown
Solenopsis xyloni	native southern fire ant	southern and southwestern U.S.	1.6–5.8 mm; bicolored with yellowish red head and thorax and dark gaster
Solenopsis geminata	tropical fire ant	southern U.S.	2.4–6 mm; highly variable with some largely yellowish or light reddish, others blackish or with mixed light and dark
Solenopsis aurea	golden or desert fire ant	southwestern U.S.	3 mm; golden yellow with pale brown bands on the margin of the gastric segments

repairs to damaged electrical equipment (e.g., short-circuited air conditioning units and traffic lights), and medical and veterinary expenses.

An invasive species native to South America, it is well established in the southeastern United States and now in California. Predictions for where it may possibly spread include all of the western states and southern British Columbia, west of the Cascade Mountains.

As their common name implies, fire ants cause a burning sensation when they sting (fig. 3.14), and for a small percentage of the population may cause a life-threatening anaphylactic reaction. Indeed, there have been

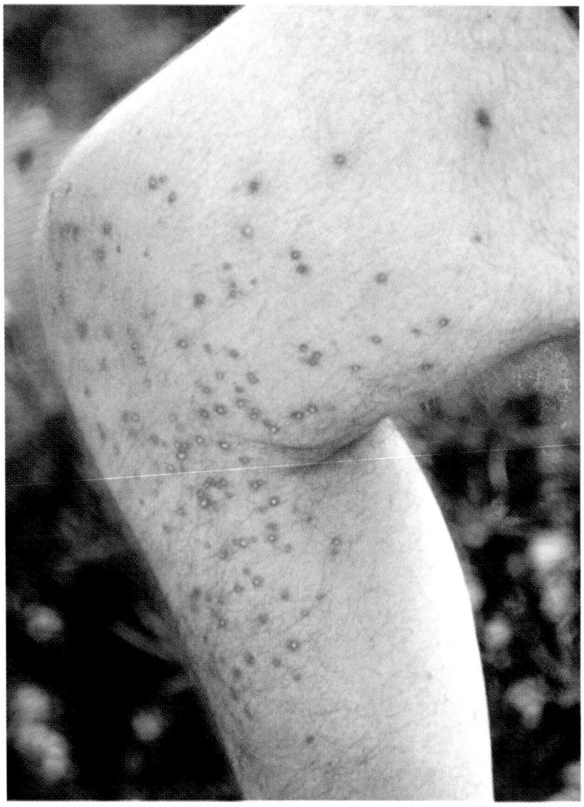

FIGURE 3.14.
Pseudopustules caused by stings of the red imported fire ant, *Solenopsis invicta*. Photo: Dan Wojick.

more than 80 deaths attributed to imported fire ant stings (Kemp et al. 2000).

Other Solenopsis Species. Allergic reactions have been reported to stings from three native fire ant species: the southern fire ant, *S. xyloni* (fig. 3.13); the desert or golden fire ant, *S. aurea*; and the tropical fire ant, *S. geminata* (Hoffman 1997). In the case of southern fire ants, two incidents that involved infants proved to be fatal (Klotz et al. 2004; Coarsey 1952).

IDENTIFICATION AND BIOLOGY

Fire ants have two nodes and 10-segmented antennae, which includes a 2-segmented antennal club. The red imported fire ant and southern fire ant have polymorphic workers ranging in size from about 2 to 5 mm. The workers of red imported fire ants are dark reddish brown, appearing almost black in direct sunlight as compared with the red and black bicoloration of southern fire ants. The tropical fire ant is often confused with the southern fire ant, but major workers of the former species have large bilobed heads. The desert fire ant is about 3 mm long and golden yellow with pale brown bands on the margin of its gastric segments (table 3.1).

Red imported fire ants have two distinct social forms based on whether the colony has one queen (monogyne) or multiple queens (polygyne). Monogyne colonies are territorial, and thus fight with other colonies of red imported fire ants. This antagonistic behavior results in nests being spaced farther apart than the nonterritorial polygyne colonies. Consequently, monogyne populations can have 40 to 150 nests per acre while polygyne colonies are closer together, with as many as 200 to 800 nests per acre. There also may be as many as 100,000 to 500,000 ants per mature

FIGURE 3.15.

Crater nest entrances of the southern fire ant, *Solenopsis xyloni* (A), and mound nest of the red imported fire ant, *Solenopsis invicta* (B). *Photos:* Courtesy of UC IPM (A); John Kabashima (B).

polygyne colony, while monogyne colonies may have 100,000 to 240,000 ants per colony. In general, an acre of a polygyne population of fire ants may contain 14 million ants weighing 25 pounds, while a monogyne population would contain roughly half that amount of ants (forming a mass about the size of a fat cat) (Macom and Porter 1996).

In the Southeast, mating flights of red imported fire ants usually take place in the spring or early summer, triggered by environmental cues which synchronize their flights over large geographic areas. Typically, they occur on warm, windless days when the sky clears after a rain. In Southern California, however, rain is a rare event and mating flights have been observed in association with irrigation, but it is not clear how much of a role this may play in the spread of imported fire ants.

The winged male and female reproductives (alates) gather in aerial swarms to mate several hundred feet off the ground. After mating, the females disperse and can sometimes be carried by wind for miles, at which point they drop to the ground, remove their wings, and search for a suitable site to excavate a nest, typically in moist soil. It takes about a year before the colony starts producing reproductives. A mature colony may produce as many as 4,000 to 6,000 reproductives per year (Vinson 1997).

Fire ants are omnivores, and in the heavily infested areas of the southeastern United States, the voracious appetite of red imported fire ants can adversely affect biodiversity by displacing native ant species and eliminating other invertebrates as well as some vertebrate species (Porter and Savignano 1990; Lofgren 1986). Interestingly, some researchers have recently proposed that the role of fire ants as competitors of native ants is exaggerated (King and Tschinkel 2008).

Colonies of southern fire ants, *Solenopsis xyloni*, are polygynous but generally smaller and their nests consist of irregular craters versus the domed mounds of red imported fire ants (fig. 3.15). They are found in the southern United States and thrive in semidisturbed habitats, sometimes becoming a nuisance pest around homes. Southern fire ants have been largely displaced by red imported fire ants in the southeastern states. Desert or golden fire ants, *Solenopsis aurea*, are not considered pests and are rarely seen due to their nocturnal habits (Taber 2000). Their range is limited to the Colorado Desert in California and north into southern Nevada along the eastern Mojave Desert (Snelling and George 1979). The tropical fire ant, *Solenopsis geminata*, has been partly displaced by the red imported fire ant but is found in some areas of the southern United States.

FIGURE 3.16.

Baits for red imported fire ants consist of corn grit and soybean oil, which act as carriers for various bait toxicants. *Photo:* John Kabashima.

Table 3.2. Common bait insecticides for imported fire ant control

ACTIVE INGREDIENT (PERCENT AI)	MODE OF ACTION	PRODUCT NAME	SPEED OF CONTROL
hydramethylnon (0.73)	metabolic inhibitor	Amdro	moderate to slow
abamectin (0.011)	IGR*	Ascend/Clinch	moderate to slow
fipronil (0.00015)	neural disrupter	Ceasefire	moderate to slow
pyriproxyfen (0.5)	IGR	Distance	slow
spinosad (0.015)	neural disrupter	products with Conserve	fast to moderate
methoprene (0.5)	IGR	Extinguish	slow
fenoxycarb (1.0)	IGR	Award	slow
indoxacarb (0.045)	neural disrupter	Advion	fast

Source: Greenberg et al. 2008; Oi 2008; Barr et al. 2005.
Note: *IGR = insect growth regulator

MANAGEMENT

More research has been devoted to developing pest management strategies for imported fire ants than for any other urban pest ant. Indeed, it is the only ant species for which a comprehensive urban integrated pest management program exists (Drees 2006). Particularly noteworthy in the realm of bait development have been the prodigious efforts of USDA-ARS scientists, who screened over 7,000 compounds as potential bait toxicants for imported fire ants (Williams et al. 2001). The toxicants are typically dissolved in soybean oil, which coats a defatted corn grit carrier to make highly palatable and effective baits for imported fire ants (fig. 3.16 and table 3.2) Southern fire ants are less attracted to baits made of corn grit and soybean oil. Better control can be achieved with the protein-base 0.9 percent hydramethylnon granular bait (Hooper et al. 1998).

Fire ant control methods are based primarily on red imported fire ant research, but many aspects are applicable to other fire ant species. Because red imported fire ant nests are often visible as mounds of excavated soil, control methods can be directed at individual colonies. Depending on the number of nests that need to be treated and on their accessibility, two approaches to applying treatments can be utilized. If only a few nests are in a limited area (e.g., less than 5 nests per 5,000 square feet), locating and treating individual nests would be reasonable. If nest densities are high or the nests cannot be located because the area is difficult to survey because of size, terrain, or thick vegetation, broadcasting bait over the infested area (without locating individual nests) is more practical.

Most fire ant baits have a very low broadcast application rate of 1 to 1.5 pounds per acre. Because individual nests do not have to be located and treated, broadcasting bait is a very efficient treatment method, both in terms of control and labor (Barr et al. 1999). However, broadcast application rates may not be effective for very small areas. For example, for 500 square feet, only 7.8 grams of bait should be broadcast at a recommended broadcast application rate of 1.5 pounds per acre, which is well below label recommendations of 10.0 to 56.7 grams per nest.

As mentioned, the visibility and accessibility of fire ant nests makes direct treatment of colonies feasible. The objective is to eliminate the colony by killing the queen and most of the stinging adult workers. If the queen is not killed or functionally sterilized, she will continue to lay eggs and the colony will recover. In the case of polygyne colonies, all the queens must be killed, thus making effective treatments more difficult. Individually treating nests or mounds is time consuming and labor-intensive, because each mound must be located and treated (Barr et al. 1999). However, colonies treated directly and properly with fast-acting insecticides can be eliminated more quickly than colonies treated with baits and residual insecticides with slow modes of action. Individual mound treatments, however, may cause the fire ants to relocate and create a new nest. Even if the queen is killed, surviving ants may still inhabit the treated nest or make a new nest until they die naturally, which may take over a month.

Individual mound treatments use insecticides that are most commonly formulated as baits, liquid drenches, granules, or dusts. In general, products formulated as drenches, granules, or dusts contain active ingredients that will often kill ants immediately on contact. Because fire ant colonies move to occupy optimal temperature strata within a nest throughout the day, treatments should be applied when the colony is concentrated near the nest surface. Thus, optimal treatment times are generally limited to when air temperatures are cool (about 65° to 75°F [18° to 24°C]) and the sun warms the nest surface. When properly treated, colonies may die within a few hours to a few days after treatment.

Bait products used for broadcast bait applications can be applied to individual nests. Because ants will distribute the bait to the colony, the emphasis with bait applications is to ensure that baits are available when and where fire ants are foraging. Bait application to individual nests is relatively simple, where the recommended amount of bait is sprinkled around the base of the nest. As with broadcast bait applications, the use of baits for individual nest treatments usually takes one to several weeks to eliminate colonies. However, there are now bait products that will kill colonies within 3 days (e.g., baits containing the insecticide indoxacarb).

Broadcast baiting and individually treating mounds with contact insecticides can be combined to take advantage of the efficiency of baits and the faster speed of kill with contact insecticides. This procedure has been called "the Two-Step Method of Do It-Yourself Fire Ant Control" (Merchant and Drees 1992). In Step 1, bait is broadcasted and allowed time to be collected by the ants and spread by trophallaxis (food sharing) through the colony. A few days later, in Step 2, a fast-acting contact insecticide, such as acephate, is applied to hazardous nests that require quick elimination.

Broadcasting residual insecticides over an infested area attempts to eliminate fire ant populations and prevent reinfestation of frequently used areas (e.g., athletic fields). The most effective materials have been nonrepellent, slow-acting contact insecticides, with residual activity of over 6 months. The absence of both repellency and the immediate death of ants facilitate insecticide contact with foraging ants and colonies located in treated areas. On the other hand, immediate death or repellency due to irritation often elicits avoidance of treated areas by fire ants (Oi and Williams 1996) and reduces control to a short-lived suppression of fire ants. Long-lasting control of imported fire ants (more than 1 year) has been achieved with a single broadcast application of granular fipronil (0.0143%) (Greenberg et al. 2003); however, granular insecticides should not be used in locations susceptible to water runoff, such as driveways, sidewalks, and street curbs.

General considerations for implementing a red imported fire ant management program include (1) confirming that fire ants are the species causing the problem and (2) determining where and what level of control is needed. Fire ant population densities and distribution will vary with the degree to which habitats are conducive to colony growth. Locating and mapping areas where control is needed will help limit potential treatment areas. Be aware of deadlines for achieving control when scheduling sites for monitoring and treatment. Many fire ant treatments take at least a few weeks to obtain population reductions.

Determining whether control is needed should be based on the tolerance of fire ants for specific land use patterns. The intensity of the control effort should reflect the potential hazard that fire ants present. This is a function of the probability of a fire ant stinging a victim and the consequences if a sting occurs (such as a lawsuit). For example, infrequent or no treatment is needed for freeway median strips; an annual broadcast application of an insect growth regulator (IGR) bait is sufficient for an infrequently used park. In contrast, for a toddler playground it may be warranted to provide a broadcast application of baits in the spring, summer, and fall, plus an individual treatment of hazardous nests with fast-acting contact insecticides or baits, and weekly monitoring for new nests or the presence of fire ants.

Evaluating and adjusting the control program is important for maintaining efficient fire ant management. Mapping areas where fire ant infestations are located, along with recording pre- and post-treatment population levels, allow the control program to be evaluated. Monitoring population levels at times when the potential for stings is high (such as the outdoor recreational season) will provide an indication of a treatment's efficacy and timeliness. Population levels can be based on nest densities, percentage of monitoring stations with fire ants, the number of sting incidents or complaints, or a combination of these indicators. Maintaining site-specific historical records of treatment regimes, dates and weather conditions during treatment applications, and population levels will permit more precise adjustments to control programs (Oi 2008).

More complex programs have been proposed that are tailored to more specific environments, such as health care facilities and other urban environments (Goddard et al. 2002; Drees et al. 2006). Treatment programs for imported fire ants that are tailored for various needs can be accessed at the Cooperative Extension System Web site, http://www.extension.org/pages/Fire_Ant_Decision_Tool:_Customized_Management_Plan.

FIGURE 3.17.
Odorous house ant, *Tapinoma sessile*, workers and queens. *Photo:* Dong-Hwan Choe.

ADDITIONAL WEB SITES FOR INFORMATION ON FIRE ANTS

A complete list of publications on fire ants by each of the scientists at the USDA-ARS-CMAVE in Gainesville, Florida, can be found at the USDA's Agricultural Research Service Web site, http://www.ars.usda.gov/Services/Services.htm?modecode=66-15-10-15.

The Texas A&M Agricultural Extension and Research Service developed "The Two- Step Method Do-It-Yourself Fire Ant Control." For more information, check the National Ag Safety Database Web site, http://www.cdc.gov/nasd/docs/d001201-d001300/d001256/d001256.html.

Research and extension publications on imported fire ants in California can be found at the UC Riverside Urban Entomology Web site, http://urban.cmsdev.ucr.edu/.

ODOROUS HOUSE ANTS

PEST STATUS

The odorous house ant (fig. 3.17) is widely distributed throughout the United States and is one of the most ecologically adaptive of all the North American ants (Fisher and Cover 2007). The wide variation in its DNA suggests that it may consist of more than one species (L. Davis Jr., pers. comm., 2007). The structural pest control industry ranks it as the number two "bad girl" in the United States (Vail et al. 2003), and some companies consider it the number one call-back pest (Barbani 2003). Geographical hotspots include the Mid-South and lower Midwest, Pacific Northwest, and Central and Northern California (Hedges 1998a). These ants have been intercepted in Hawaii but have not become established there like the Argentine ant.

It is not known why odorous house ants are becoming more common and possibly undergoing a range expansion, but contributing factors may include (1) increased use of perimeter treatments, resulting in their competitive release from other ant species; (2) increased use of landscape mulch, providing them with prime nesting sites; and possibly (3) higher temperatures due to global warming (Scharf et al. 2004).

FIGURE 3.18.

Large colony of odorous house ants found between layers of stacked siding (A) and close-up of worker with larvae (B). *Photos:* Karen Vail and Gary Alpert.

IDENTIFICATION AND BIOLOGY

Odorous house ants are often confused with Argentine ants; however, their petiolar node can be used to differentiate them (see Ant Key, appendix B). On the odorous house ant it is flattened and hidden from view by the gaster as compared with a conspicuously visible vertical node on the Argentine ant. In addition, the odorous house ant emits a distinctly pungent odor of rotten coconut when crushed, unlike the slight musty odor emitted by crushed Argentine ants. Odorous house ants are also sometimes confused with *Liometopum luctuosum*; however, this species has a distinct

vertical node that is somewhat hidden by the gaster, which is covered with fine hairs that give it a velvety appearance. The size and color of odorous house ants are quite variable (Fisher and Cover 2007).

Although native to North America, the odorous house ant shares three characteristics with exotic tramp species (Passera 1994): polygyny, colony multiplication by budding (along with mating flights), and opportunistic nesting habits. Similar to Argentine ants, odorous house ants exhibit seasonal polydomy with an annual fission-fusion cycle (Buczkowski and Bennett 2008): colonies merge in winter and then break up and disperse into smaller colonies in spring, sometimes extending over entire habitats. Additionally, they are dispersed central-place foragers (Buczkowksi and Bennett 2006): flow of food is decentralized, moving in many directions according to need. However, the interchange of food and workers between nests is more restricted than in Argentine ants (Buczkowski and Bennett 2006).

Odorous house ants can be found nesting both indoors and outdoors, occupying almost any location that provides shelter (e.g., in or under landscape timbers, under the bark of logs or stumps, between layers of stacked siding) (fig. 3.18), and in leaves or under garbage cans as well as structural voids. Indoor nesting sites include areas with access to moisture, such as the bathroom and kitchen and potted plants. Colonies range in size from a few hundred individuals to many thousands. Because their colonies may have multiple queens and are capable of budding, they may spread throughout a structure or landscape.

The network of nests is a consequence of their unique ability to splinter or bud new colonies. When a colony is ready to bud, one or more of the many queens in the parent colony leaves the nest with some workers and brood to form a new colony. Colonies are sensitive to chemical and mechanical disturbance and will readily move to another nest site or split into satellite colonies (Barbani and Fell 2002).

Odorous house ants are omnivorous but have a distinct preference for sweets, and they forage both day and night (Barbani 2003). Their foraging trails can be quite extensive, ranging from 33 to 157 feet long (Buczkowski and Bennett 2008).

MANAGEMENT

For odorous house ant control, Vail et al. (2003) combined a liquid bait delivery system with a perimeter spray treatment and compared it with the bait and spray alone. The spray consisted of fipronil applied 1 foot up and 1 foot out from the foundation. The bait was an experimental sweetened liquid containing 1.3 percent borax that was placed in the landscape outside the spray zone. The combination treatment was the most effective at eliminating the ants indoors.

Other highly effective baits include gel formulations of indoxacarb or thiamethoxam, which are available to PMPs. Because there is little or no interchange of workers between some nests, it is important to bait as many trails as possible. When baits are used in ant control, it is important for the homeowner to understand that ants foraging on bait should not be disturbed.

Another very effective strategy to reduce both indoor and outdoor odorous house ant activity is a spray combination consisting of an application of fipronil on the outside perimeter and an interior spot application of chlorfenapyr (K. Vail, pers. comm., 2008), the so-called *Inside-Out* ant control program.

Over-the-counter insecticides containing pyrethroids are not recommended for odorous

house ant control. They are repellent to ants and may cause the colony to splinter, making the infestation more difficult to control.

CARPENTER ANTS AND VELVETY TREE ANTS

PEST STATUS

Nationwide, carpenter ant control generates more revenue for the structural pest management industry than control for any other ant. They amount to 35 percent of the pest control business for one large company in the Pacific Northwest (Hansen and Klotz 2005); and according to Leonard Douglen (2005), Executive Director of the New Jersey Pest Management Association, they "pose a major threat to homes, apartments, and other structures throughout the northeast."

In forest ecosystems, carpenter ants play a major role in initiating the decomposition of wood (fig. 3.19). In urban settings they can cause significant damage to structures, trees, and wood used in landscaping. Unlike termites, ants do not consume wood but rather excavate it for their nests and runways. There are 50 species of carpenter ants in the United States and Canada, of which about half are nuisance or structural pests (Hansen and Klotz 2005). The most destructive species in the western United States are *Camponotus modoc* and *C. vicinus* (fig. 3.20). There are several other large carpenter ants as well as some that are smaller in size (table 3.3). Many of these are considered chiefly as nuisance pests.

Velvety tree ants are another group of wood-destroying ants that are commonly mistaken for carpenter ants (because of their excavations in wood) or for odorous house ants (because of the similarity in the odor they produce). There are three species of *Liometopum* inhabiting the western and southwestern United States: the velvety tree ant, *L. occidentale* (fig. 3.21), which is found along the West Coast from British Columbia to Baja California at sea level up to elevations of 4,800 feet (Snelling and George 1979); *L. luctuosum*, which ranges from Wyoming to western Texas to Nevada and California (Gulmahamad 1995) and the Pacific Northwest, typically at higher elevations from 2,000 to 7,000 feet (Creighton 1950), but has

FIGURE 3.19.

Dead tree infested by a colony of western black carpenter ants, *Camponotus modoc*. *Photo:* Laurel Hansen.

FIGURE 3.20.

Workers of *Camponotus modoc* (A) and *C. vicinus* (B). *Photos:* Gary Alpert.

FIGURE 3.21.

Worker of velvety tree ant, *Liometopum occidentale*. *Photo:* Courtesy of UC IPM.

FIGURE 3.22.

Fine-textured sawdust produced by the pine tree ant, *Liometopum luctuosum*. *Photo:* John Klotz.

Table 3.3. Some common western species of carpenter ants and their geographic distribution

CAMPONOTUS SPECIES	GEOGRAPHICAL DISTRIBUTION
C. modoc	western U.S., southwestern Canada
C. vicinus	western U.S., Mexico to southern Canada
C. laevigatus	western North America
C. essigi	northwestern Mexico to southern Canada
C. clarithorax	CA, OR, and northern part of Baja CA, Mexico
C. sayi	southern U.S. and northern Mexico

been reported at elevations down to 1,000 feet (unpubl. Hansen); and *L. apiculatum*, which ranges from Colorado through Arizona, New Mexico, and Texas (Gulmahamad 1995) in foothill areas up to 7,000 feet. These species may excavate wood and insulation, producing fine-textured sawdust and insulation particles (fig. 3.22). For example, in the San Bernardino Mountain communities in Southern California, *L. luctuosum*, also known as the *pine tree ant*, frequently infests homes; and one PMP states that it is the bread and butter of his pest control business. Heavy infestations of this species have also been observed in the Cascade Mountains and eastern Washington

FIGURE 3.23.

Note the rounded upper surface of the mesosoma, which is characteristic of carpenter ants. *Photo:* Courtesy of UC IPM.

and Oregon. Their significance as structural pests has probably been underestimated due to confusion with other ants.

IDENTIFICATION AND BIOLOGY

Carpenter Ants. As is characteristic of the ants belonging to the subfamily Formicinae, carpenter ants possess a circle of hairs on the tip of the abdomen, which is used like a brush to deposit their odor trail. The petiole has a single node and the dorsum of the mesosoma has a smooth, even profile (fig. 3.23). Carpenter ant workers are polymorphic and range in size from small minors to large majors commonly called *soldiers*. The different sizes are the result of the larvae receiving different amounts of food. The majors receive the lion's share and in some species become the biggest workers of all North American ants. The queens are

even larger than the major workers but males are smaller. Both winged forms have a humpbacked appearance due to their massive wing muscles. *C. modoc* are black and workers range in size from 6 mm to 13 mm in length. *C. vicinus* is similar in size but variable in color, most commonly with a red mesosoma and black head, gaster, and legs. *C. laevigatus* has a shiny, jet-black appearance, and unlike the other species is active primarily during the daytime. *C. essigi*, *C. sayi*, and *C. clarithorax* are smaller in size with majors less than 8 mm. These do not cause the massive damage of the larger carpenter ants but are annoying as nuisance pests, particularly in the late winter and early spring when they become active within structures.

Carpenter ants cannot sting but will bite and spray formic acid. Their powerful jaws are used for excavating wood, and their common name "carpenter" is derived from the smooth, almost sandpapered appearance of their tunnels and galleries (fig. 3.24). They nest in both living and dead trees as well as in fallen logs and stumps. Homes built near forests are particularly vulnerable to infestation (fig. 3.25), and new homes are often invaded and damaged even before construction is complete. Being opportunistic, the carpenter ant will also nest in structural voids and soft insulation, both fiberglass and foam core, which make ideal substrates for excavating nests. They sometimes become a nuisance due to the noise they make when excavating wood or these other materials.

FIGURE 3.24.

Their common name, carpenter ants, is derived from the smooth almost sand-papered appearance of their nest tunnels and galleries. *Photo:* Laurel Hansen.

FIGURE 3.25.

Prime habitat for velvety tree ants and carpenter ants. *Photo:* Laurel Hansen.

FIGURE 3.26.
Knot holes and dead sections of trees are common nesting sites for carpenter ants. *Photo:* John Klotz.

Mature colonies of *C. modoc* can have 50,000 workers but typically only one queen; those of *C. vicinus* have multiple queens, with as many as 40 queens and 100,000 workers reported (Akre et al. 1994). Mature colonies are partitioned into main and satellite nests. In structural infestations, it is common to have the main nest located outside in a live or dead tree (fig. 3.26), stump, or wood buried in the soil. The queen, eggs, and young larvae are located here where there is sufficient moisture. Satellite nests are often located within structures and contain workers, older brood, and reproductives, which can live in drier environments. The main nest may also contain workers and reproductives. The various nests of a colony are connected by trails (fig. 3.27) to maintain communication—

and if a satellite nest is eliminated, it may soon be replaced with more workers from the main nest.

Colony multiplication is achieved by mating flights (fig. 3.28), which occur in the spring. Flights are synchronized over large geographic areas and triggered by environmental factors such as photoperiod and changes in temperature or humidity (Hansen and Klotz 2005). After dispersing from a mating swarm, an inseminated queen finds a suitable nest site, breaks off her wings, and initiates a colony (fig. 3.29). The queen does not leave the nest to forage; instead, she metabolizes her fat reserves and wing muscles in order to survive, produce her first clutch of eggs, and feed the first larvae. The colony grows slowly at first and requires several years to reach maturity and produce winged forms.

Carpenter ants are omnivorous and are particularly attracted to honeydew, a high-energy liquid excreted by various kinds of plant-sucking insects (hemipterans) such as

FIGURE 3.27.
In addition to their odor trail, carpenter ants frequently cut physical trails through turf. *Photo:* Laurel Hansen.

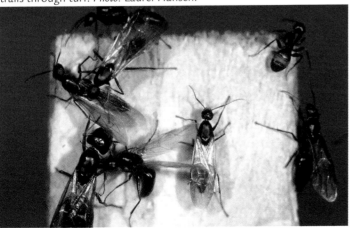

FIGURE 3.28.
Winged male and female *Camponotus modoc* reproductives preparing for a mating flight. *Photo:* Laurel Hansen.

FIGURE 3.29.
Newly mated *Camponotus modoc* queen with her first brood. *Photo:* Laurel Hansen.

aphids and scales. Honeydew contains sugars, amino acids, minerals, and vitamins. The digestive system of carpenter ants is specialized for handling a liquid diet. The expandable crop, also known as the "social stomach," is particularly noteworthy. During the process of trophallaxis, an ant regurgitates some of its crop contents to share with a nestmate (fig. 3.30), who in turn shares with other nestmates, thereby distributing the food through the colony.

Foraging carpenter ants deposit a trail pheromone that is produced in the hindgut, which provides a chemical path for the ants to follow between their nest and foraging resources. The odor trail is an important orientation cue, particularly for species that are primarily nocturnal. In these species, there is some level of activity during the day but around dusk there is a burst of activity when workers start pouring out of the nest to begin foraging. Another peak in activity occurs around dawn when all the foragers are returning to the nest. The change in light intensity at sunset and sunrise appears to be the trigger for these spikes in activity. Carpenter ants forage in trees and bushes so their trails are frequently laid down along branches and twigs. However, when they enter the home environment, structural edges and utility lines become their guidelines.

Velvety Tree Ants. Velvety tree ants also nest and forage in trees: *L. occidentale* typically in deciduous trees such as oak, cottonwood, and sycamore, and *L. luctuosum* in conifers. Like carpenter ants they are polymorphic but considerably smaller (2 to 5 mm in length).

FIGURE 3.30.

Trophallaxis between workers of *Camponotus modoc*. *Photo:* Reiner Pospischil.

They have one node on the petiole and a smooth dorsal mesosomal profile. However, unlike carpenter ants they lack the circular fringe of hairs on the tip of the abdomen, instead having a ventral cloacal slit that is characteristic of the species belonging to the subfamily Dolichoderinae. The dense fine hairs on their abdomen give these species a velvety appearance. *L. luctuosum* and *L. apiculatum* are dark brown, and *L. occidentale* is bicolored with a reddish-orange thoracic region and black head and abdomen. *L. luctuosum* is the same color as odorous house ants but just slightly larger, and it may be confused with this species.

When their nest is disturbed, velvety tree ants come pouring out, excitedly running about with their jaws opened wide ready to bite and their abdomens tilted up emitting a pheromone. This pheromone has the same odor as the one odorous house ants produce, but more pungent. Their colonies may consist of multiple, moveable satellite nests and are referred to as polydomous. Individual colonies may attain tremendous population levels over large areas.

Foraging columns an inch wide and several hundred feet long are not uncommon. Like carpenter ants, their foraging may occur during the day and night; however, velvety tree ants are more commonly seen in daylight hours. They have cryptic habits so their trails often go unnoticed because they are concealed beneath siding, between boards, or on branches or wires touching the structure from above. They are omnivorous, with a diet that includes honeydew from aphids and scales, as well as small arthropods that they prey upon. There are few publications on the biology of velvety tree ants and additional research is needed.

Velvety tree ants can cause significant damage to both insulation and wood (fig. 3.31). In mountain homes, tongue-and-groove ceilings made of wooden panels are common and the insulation above it is a favorite excavation site for these ants. Insulation in attic spaces is also frequently infested. Their excavations have a much finer texture than that of carpenter ants, and homeowners often complain of an odor associated with it.

FIGURE 3.31.

Frass produced by infestation of pine tree ants, *Liometopum luctuosum*. *Photo:* Mike Nolan.

FIGURE 3.32.

Railroad ties provide ideal nesting sites for carpenter ants and should be inspected and treated if infested. *Photo:* John Klotz.

MANAGEMENT

There are four components of an effective pest management program for carpenter ants (Hansen and Klotz 2005), which can also be applied to managing velvety tree ants: client interview, inspection, treatment, and follow-up evaluation.

Interview. A program to manage carpenter ants or velvety tree ants should always begin with an interview of the client. A good interview can provide critical information on the history and details of an infestation, which may help the PMP to locate nests and other potential hot spots. A comprehensive list of

suggested questions that the PMP can adapt to any circumstance can be found in table 6.7 in *Carpenter Ants of the United States and Canada* (Hansen and Klotz 2005).

Inspection. The PMP should thoroughly inspect the property and draw up an inspection diagram, noting on it the location of foraging trails, potential nest sites, and conditions conducive to infestation. This diagram can be helpful in educating the client as well as designing a treatment strategy.

In the case of velvety tree ants, there may be sufficient ant activity during the day to obtain a fairly accurate picture of the problem. Many species of carpenter ants, however, are nocturnal—so an inspection after sunset might be recommended. This could be billed as an added service or, in the case of difficult accounts, as an integral part of the service.

The PMP needs to communicate to the client the conditions that may be contributing to their infestation, such as

- firewood stacked on the ground
- deck or crawlspace pillars in contact with the soil
- landscaping timbers near the structure (fig. 3.32)
- roof and gutter leaks
- plumbing leaks
- improper drainage (for example, flat roofs on houses are at high risk for ant infestation because of drainage problems)
- wooden fences in contact with the house

In addition, the PMP should enlist the help of the client in implementing any preventive cultural control measures, such as

- removing branches, vines, or foliage touching the structure or in contact with cable or electrical lines, which may serve as access points
- avoiding landscape mulches over 2 to 3 inches in depth, which make for good nesting sites for new colonies
- ensuring proper ventilation in basements and crawl spaces, and installing vapor barriers where needed

Treatment. Currently, the most effective chemical control measure for wood-destroying ants is a perimeter treatment with a slow-acting spray such as fipronil, and its efficacy is maximized when it is applied during peak

FIGURE 3.33.

All access points to the structure must be inspected and treated for wood-destroying ants. *Photo:* John Klotz.

FIGURE 3.34.

Treating tree trunks and utility lines can deter ants from gaining access to a structure. *Photo:* John Klotz.

foraging activity so that the ants pick up the active ingredient and transfer it to other ants, eventually spreading it through the colony. A thorough application is necessary, treating all potential access points to the structure, which includes around the foundation, deck posts (fig. 3.33), and stairwells. In some cases it might be necessary to make additional spot applications of insecticide inside, for example, with an injection of insecticidal dust into a void space to eliminate a satellite colony. Several dust formulations (e.g., 0.05% deltamethrin, silica

compounds, borates) are labeled for wall injection. It is important to review current labels and follow label directions.

In order to maximize the effectiveness of a perimeter treatment, the PMP should try to remove or treat with pyrethroids (e.g., bifenthrin, cyfluthrin, deltamethrin) as many avenues and structural guidelines (e.g., conduits, pipes, wires) as possible that the ants might use to enter the structure (fig. 3.34). For example, branches touching the structure should be removed, and cable and phone lines should be treated so that ants cannot bridge the structure from above. Tree trunks in the yard should be treated because these ants nest and forage in trees. Decorative posts, railroad ties, and wooded landscape should also be treated.

Carpenter ants sometimes become active inside structures during their dormant season, which typically lasts from late fall to early spring. The warmer interior temperature may stimulate over-wintering males to leave the nest prematurely on mating flights. Attracted to light, these winged ants often move to windows, and locating their nests can be difficult because most of the colony remains inactive. In some cases the nest can be located by tapping on potential nesting sites in wall or ceiling voids and then listening for any rustling noises of ants. Dust applications may be required to treat these interior infestations, particularly during dormant times of the year when the ants are not foraging (Hansen 2007).

Baiting for carpenter ants is an alternate treatment. There are a variety of gels, liquids, and granules available to PMPs. If baits are used, prebaiting is recommended. Small samples of bait should be offered to foraging ants to determine if they feed on them (fig. 3.35). Baits should be placed in areas where the ants are actively foraging so that the ants' response to them can be observed. Ideally, a bait preference test would be conducted after sunset when the ants are most active. However, even during the day there are always a few

FIGURE 3.35.

Bait preference test for carpenter ants. *Photo:* John Klotz.

foragers that are active. Although research on baiting for velvety tree ants is lacking, there are a number of baits available to PMPs that might be effective; and, as with carpenter ants, any potential baits should be tested for preference and monitored for feeding.

Follow-up Evaluation. The final component in a pest management program for wood-destroying ants is an evaluation by the PMP to determine whether the treatment was effective and satisfactory to the client. For homes located in heavily forested areas, an annual inspection should be instituted.

CHAPTER FOUR

Occasional and Emerging Urban Ant Pests of California

PHARAOH ANTS AND THIEF ANTS

PEST STATUS

Pharaoh ants, *Monomorium pharaonis* (fig. 4.1), are particularly common in southern and southwestern areas of the country such as Florida, Texas, and Southern California. Smith (1965) noted that "the Pharaoh ant probably occurs in every town or city of commercial importance in the United States," and the situation has probably not changed much since this observation was made over 40 years ago.

They are considered to be tramp ants, possibly originating in India and subsequently spreading throughout the world by commerce. They thrive in disturbed habitats, living in close association with humans. Once established, Pharaoh ants can spread quickly due partly to colony budding but more importantly to people inadvertently transporting them. Consequently, they often become major problems throughout large building complexes, such as apartments and hospitals. They have been reported to carry various infectious bacteria including *Pseudomonas*, *Staphyloccocus*, *Salmonella*, *Clostridium*, and *Streptococcus*, and have been known to infest intravenous units and sterile dressings (Beatson 1972, 1973).

Thief ants, *Solenopsis molesta*, are commonly confused with Pharaoh ants, so their significance as structural pests is unknown (Hedges 1998a).

FIGURE 4.1.

A Pharaoh ant worker, *Monomorium pharaonis. Photo:* Reiner Pospischil.

IDENTIFICATION AND BIOLOGY

The Pharaoh ant is easily confused with the thief ant because workers of both species are monomorphic and similar in size and color. Both species are small (about 2 mm), similar in color, and have two nodes on the petiole. The number of segments on their antennae and antennal clubs can be used to differentiate them: the thief ant has a 10-segmented antenna with a two-segmented club, while the Pharaoh ant has a 12-segmented antenna with a 3-segmented club. Thief ants were given their name because they nest near or within the nests of other ant species, robbing them of their food stores and their young. Occasionally they become pests indoors but infestations are typically small and localized (Hedges 1998a).

Pharaoh ants share some important characteristics of

37

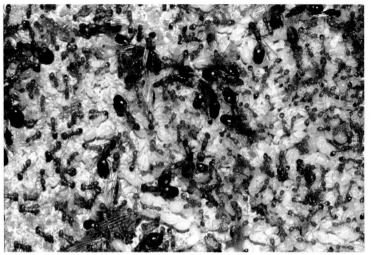

FIGURE 4.2.

Multi-queen colonies of Pharaoh ants have a high reproductive potential. *Photo:* Reiner Pospischil.

FIGURE 4.3.

Outdoor colony of Pharaoh ants in a territorial dispute with red imported fire ants. *Photo:* John Klotz.

colony dynamics and behavior with other exotic tramp ants (Passera 1994): (1) colonies have multiple queens (fig. 4.2) and achieve colony multiplication by budding, and (2) there is little aggression towards individuals from different nests. In temperate climates, Pharaoh ant nests are typically found indoors. Being opportunistic, they will nest in any crack or crevice with sufficient warmth and high humidity. They are frequently found in kitchens and bathrooms near a source of water such as around toilets, sinks, heating ducts, and pipes. In the tropics or subtropical areas, they are also found nesting outdoors (fig. 4.3).

Pharaoh ants are omnivores (fig. 4.4) but have finicky dietary habits and periodically change their food preference. For example, laboratory colonies fed a carbohydrate diet will shift to proteins if given a choice and vice versa if fed proteins (Edwards and Abraham 1990). They can forage over long distances. One of the authors (H.F.) witnessed them foraging 10 stories up an elevator shaft in a Houston hospital to gain access to open wounds of burn patients. Consequently, when these ants are found foraging in a structure, their nest may be located at some distance from the food source.

MANAGEMENT

Some of the most effective home remedies in ant control were developed for Pharaoh ants. These were baits composed of various foods mixed with an active ingredient. Bait development has been a primary focus because the sprays available at the time caused colonies to fragment and disperse, creating even more severe problems (Vail 1997). With the advent of slow-acting residual sprays, however, this concern has been alleviated.

Various foods and active ingredients have been used to make toxic baits that are attractive to Pharaoh ants. Newton (1980) used either fresh or dried powdered liver mixed with 10 percent icing sugar and 10 percent boric acid (later reduced to 5% boric acid). Wright and Stout (1981) recommended 2 percent boric acid plus corn syrup. Edwards (1985) developed a highly successful baiting program for Pharaoh ants using the IGR methoprene (0.5%). He mixed it with raw liver and honey (1:1 w/w). By mixing protein and carbohydrate together, his objective was to provide a more attractive and longer-lasting bait than either component alone would provide. A mixture of 1 percent boric acid in 10 percent sucrose water significantly reduced structural infestations of Pharaoh ants (Klotz et al. 1997). The lower concentration of boric acid was used in this study to promote better penetration of the active ingredient into the colonies.

Some of the commercial baits used by PMPs for Pharaoh ants contain metabolic inhibitors and neural disrupters such as hydramethylnon and indoxacarb. Metabolic inhibitors are faster acting than either methoprene or boric acid yet sufficiently slow-acting to penetrate the colony (Haack 1991). The delayed action of toxicants exploits the recruitment behavior of ants to

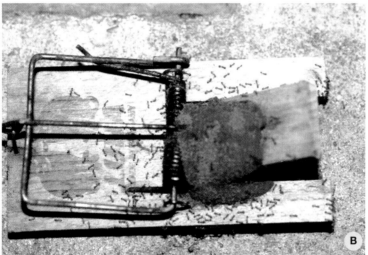

FIGURE 4.4.

Pharaoh ants have an omnivorous diet as shown feeding on a dead cockroach (A) and on cheese (B). *Photos:* Reiner Pospischil.

FIGURE 4.5.

Prebaiting with peanut butter (A) to locate Pharaoh ant hot spots (B). *Photos:* David Williams.

bring the active ingredient into the colony and distribute it to other workers, brood, and potentially the queens. The longer delay of IGRs allows the toxicant more time to spread throughout polygne colonies that may have several nest sites (Oi et al. 2000). Other active ingredients that are now available for Pharaoh ant baits include fipronil, abamectin, and pyriproxyfen (Oi 2008).

Bait placement is critical in Pharaoh ant control. To be most effective, a prebaiting program with nontoxic baits is recommended to determine where infestations are localized. Small pieces of raw liver or dabs of peanut butter, mint apple jelly, or honey placed on index cards make good monitors for Pharaoh ants (fig. 4.5). Cards should be placed in potential hot spots such as areas where the ants might be searching for food or moisture. For example, foragers often search windowsills for dead insects; kitchen counters and cabinets where food crumbs may accumulate; and pipes and fixtures associated with sinks, bathtubs, showers, and toilets. Pharaoh ants will also follow wires in voids and sometimes emerge through switch plates. After an hour or more, the cards should be checked for ant activity and, if present, replaced with toxic bait.

Avoiding spray applications for Pharaoh ants used to be a standard caveat in structural pest control because spraying caused colonies to splinter, thereby making the problem worse. Recently, however, laboratory studies by Buczkowski et al. (2005) and field studies by Oi (2005) demonstrated that the new slow-acting residual insecticides, such as fipronil and chlorfenapyr, do not cause colonies to satellite and can be used effectively to control structural infestations of Pharaoh ants. Consequently, PMPs now have the option of using these active ingredients in spray formulations for both indoor (chlorfenapyr) and outdoor (fipronil) treatments for Pharaoh ants.

THATCHING, WOOD, AND FIELD ANTS

PEST STATUS

Formica is by far the largest genus of ants in North America, including over 100 species. The genus is badly in need of revision and is generally placed into seven species groups (Fisher and Cover 2007). These species are important predators on other insects such as caterpillars, and in some cases these ants become significant biological control agents. They also herd and maintain aphid colonies on various trees and other plants. They may injure seedling trees by girdling the trunk at ground level, particularly fruit trees located near their nests. Additionally, they have been known to damage the buds of apple, pear, and plum in the spring (Akre and Antonelli 1992). The ants cannot sting but will bite with their sharp mandibles, which are capable of piercing the skin. They spray formic acid into the wound, creating a burning sensation (Blum and Hermann 1978). These ants may become a problem if a nest is located near the foundation of a house or in a garden where the homeowner may come into contact with them. However, when nests are not located in the immediate vicinity of a structure or not causing other problems, their colonies should be left undisturbed because of their beneficial attributes.

FIGURE 4.6.

Worker of *Formica* species (*Rufa* group). *Photo:* Laurel Hansen.

IDENTIFICATION AND BIOLOGY

This extremely varied group of ants, collectively known as *Formica* spp. (fig. 4.6), range in size from 2.5 to 9 mm. They are polymorphic with conspicuous ocelli and the larger workers resemble carpenter ants; however, the shape of the mesosomal dorsum is notched rather than smoothly convex. As with other members of the subfamily Formicinae, *Formica* has one node on the petiole and a circlet of hairs at the tip of the abdomen. Their color varies from red and black to entirely black. They may be confused with *Lasius* or moisture ants. The propodeal spiracle of *Formica* is a narrow slit while the spiracle of *Lasius* is round, and the latter group is generally smaller (2 to 4.5 mm) (Wheeler and Wheeler 1986).

Some species build mounds of thatch, which capture light rays (fig. 4.7). The thatch consists of small sticks, grass stems, leaves, and pine or fir needles. Within these nests the temperature varies according to depth and time of day, and the ants continually move brood from place to place to keep them at an optimal temperature (Wheeler 1910). Other species nest in rotten logs or wood debris, sometimes in nests originally occupied by carpenter ants. As the wood deteriorates from moisture and wood decay, the carpenter ants evacuate and the wood ants replace them. The species commonly known as *field ants* locate their nest entirely in the soil, sometimes under rocks and landscaping timbers. They will forage on

FIGURE 4.7.

Thatching ant mound. *Photo:* Laurel Hansen.

FIGURE 4.8.

Pavement ant worker. *Photo:* Reiner Pospischil.

FIGURE 4.9.

Pavement ant mounds along a concrete edge. *Photo:* Laurel Hansen.

decks, patios, sidewalks, and in lawns around structures.

Colonies of *Formica* are typically polygynous (many-queened), and reproductive swarms usually occur in mid to late summer. Miscellaneous behaviors occur among species, including slave-making, temporary social parasitism, and reproduction by budding (Wheeler and Wheeler 1986). Many species are social parasites, meaning that they invade other ant nests to acquire workers.

These ants will sometimes invade a structure beneath the lower edge of siding and create satellite nests in wall voids. Evidence of their presence will be small bits of thatch or debris dropping from behind an electrical outlet plate. If ants have invaded a wall void, a dust application of boric acid or silica compounds may be injected into the void. Nests located near a structure can be treated with a liquid or granular formulation by thoroughly treating the surface of the nest according to label recommendations. If the mound is more than a foot high, it should be raked down before applying the insecticide to insure that it reaches all the workers and queens.

Baits have been used to control a few species of *Formica*, but more research on bait preference and efficacy is needed (Klotz et al. 2008).

PAVEMENT ANTS

PEST STATUS

Pavement ants belong to the genus *Tetramorium*. *Tetramorium* sp. E, formerly called *T. caespitum* (Schlick-Steiner et al. 2006), is native to Europe but is now found widely throughout temperate North America, including California. *Tetramorium tsushimae* is a related, highly polygynous species, originally from Asia and currently restricted to Missouri and Illinois in North America. The early colonists are thought to have introduced pavement ants into North America from Europe (Smith 1965) (fig. 4.8). They have become established throughout the United States, particularly in urban areas. Colonies nest in soil under rocks and concrete, and are particularly troublesome along driveways, patios, and sidewalks where they deposit small, irregular piles of sand and soil (fig.4.9). They are found in rocky areas of landscapes and are commonly found around or between masonry walls of the foundation (Smith 1965). Ants sometimes enter structures through cracks in the foundation or concrete floors. However, pavement ants do not damage structures but can become a nuisance both inside and outside. The ants will forage for food and water within structures. Adverse medical reactions to their stings have been reported in some heavily infested areas (fig. 4.10).

IDENTIFICATION AND BIOLOGY

Pavement ants have two nodes, a small stinger, and a pair of spines on the back of the mesosoma. The exoskeleton on the head and mesosoma is heavily grooved with longitudinal ridges. Their color varies from brown to black, and workers are monomorphic (2.5 to 3 mm). In various species, both monogynous (single-queened) and polygynous (many-queened) colonies have been reported (Klotz et al. 2008), and the reproductives commonly leave the nest on mating flights in late June and July. Colony multiplication can also occur by budding.

These ants are omnivorous and feed on both dead and live insects, honeydew, seeds, and nectar. Within structures they will feed on various household foods such as nuts,

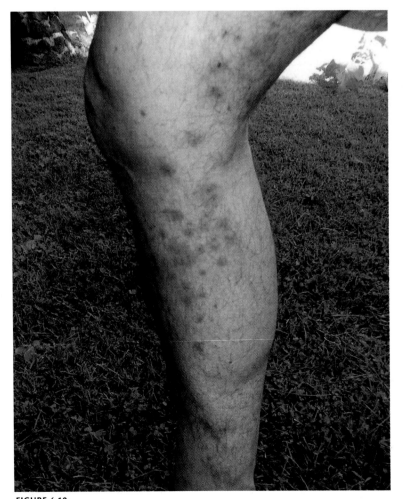

FIGURE 4.10.

Pavement ant stings. *Photo:* Laurel Hansen.

potato chips, cheese, honey, and bread, with a preference for meat or grease (Wheeler and Wheeler 1986). Their foraging trails are often established under rocks and concrete and are difficult to locate. There are generally many nest entrances, and ant activity often occurs when the entrances are not exposed to direct sunlight.

MANAGEMENT

Pavement ants can be managed by applying baits (Pinto 1990) or perimeter sprays (Scharf et al. 2004). Sweetened gels or liquids and Pharaoh ant baits have been used effectively to control pavement ants (Pinto 1990; Mampe 1993; Gerald Wegner, pers. comm., 2004). As their colonies are often very large, multiple bait applications are often necessary. Trails and entry points need to be located for proper bait placement.

Nesting sites along driveways, patios, and sidewalks can be sprayed directly by application directly to the nests following label recommendations. It is important to locate all nesting sites that may extend into landscaped areas under rocks, slabs, and landscaping timbers. Inspection should include expansion joints and doorway entrances. It may be necessary to lift items in contact with the soil in inspections and treatment. Cracks in slab floors, foundations, and concrete walls should be sealed to prevent entry of the ants and thus avoid reinfestation (Hedges 1998a).

BIG-HEADED ANTS

PEST STATUS

Big-headed ants, *Pheidole* spp., belong to one of the largest and most diverse ant genera, with over 600 species described in the New World (Wilson 2003). Most notorious is the big-headed ant, *P. megacephala* (fig. 4.11), also known as the *coastal brown ant,* which is listed among "100 of the World's Worst Invasive Alien Species" on the Global Invasive Species Database (http://www. invasivespecies.net/database/species/search. asp?st=100ss&fr=1&str). Originating in Africa, it thrives in tropical and subtropical climates throughout the world. In the United States, it is a major agricultural pest in Hawaii, where

FIGURE 4.11.
Major and minor workers of *Pheidole megacephala*. *Photo:* Reiner Pospischil.

FIGURE 4.12.
Major and minor workers of *Pheidole megacephala* feeding on a cockroach.
Photo: Reiner Pospischil.

it infests pineapple groves to tend mealybugs (Taniguchi et al. 2005), and an urban pest in Florida, especially southern parts of the state where it is probably the number one structural pest ant (Warner and Scheffrahn 2007). Most complaints arise from the unsightly piles of excavated soil that they create in nesting sites along sidewalks, driveways, and foundations, and the foragers that may be a nuisance particularly when they are found indoors. They also construct mud tubes that can be mistaken

for termites; however, the mud tube is often fragile and falls apart easily when prodded, unlike termite tubes. *P. megacephala* has been found on the Channel Islands (McGlynn 1999) off the coast of Southern California, and it could become a serious pest. However, two factors present formidable challenges for this invasive species to gain a foothold in California: its tropical origin and the omnipresence of its mortal enemy, Argentine ants, on the mainland. A few native species such as *P. hyatti* have been reported as occasional household pests in California (Ebeling 1975).

IDENTIFICATION AND BIOLOGY

The common name, big-headed ants, refers to the extraordinarily large heads of the soldier caste. Minor workers resemble imported fire ants but can be distinguished from them by their propodeal spines and 12-segmented antenna with 3-segmented club versus the fire ants' lack of spines and their 10-segmented antenna with 2-segmented club. *P. megacephala* have two nodes that are brownish yellow and the soldiers have large, heart-shaped heads (Wilson 2003), with the front half sculptured and the back half smooth and shiny (Warner and Scheffrahn 2007). Workers of *P. hyatti* are light to dark reddish (Ebeling 1975) and emit a rank, fetid odor when crushed (Snelling and George 1979).

Colonies of *P. megacephala* can reach tremendous size, with huge extended nests and multiple queens forming a supercolony (Hedges 1997). Their nests are often found along the edges of sidewalks and resemble those of red imported fire ants (Warner and Scheffrahn 2007). Colony multiplication is achieved by budding or mating flights, and in tropical and semitropical climates brood production is year round (Warner and Scheffrahn 2007). Foragers collect honeydew and feed on dead insects (fig. 4.12) and soil invertebrates.

Native California species are all ground dwelling in open, dry habitats and most are seed harvesters (Ward 2005). *P. hyatti* is nocturnal and has an omnivorous diet, preferring seeds with high oil content (Snelling and George 1979).

MANAGEMENT

Taniguchi (pers. comm. 2009) has tested most of the red imported fire ant baits on *P. megacephala* and found them to be highly effective. Using bait stations to deliver hydramethylnon, he eliminated infestations in Hawaiian pineapple fields. Granular baits were also effective in other field tests conducted by Warner and Scheffrahn (2008), who also evaluated residual spray treatments and concluded that more water volume was needed to penetrate ground cover and soil in order to kill subterranean ants. Reinfestation from surrounding areas is always a problem, so it is critical to treat the entire supercolony.

WHITE-FOOTED ANTS

PEST STATUS

White-footed ants (fig. 4.13) is the common name of a widespread tramp ant species of the Old World Tropics, *Technomyrmex albipes*, and was the name applied to several very similar species studied throughout the world (Bolton 2007). Thus, before 2007, many publications on *Technomyrmex albipes* may actually have been referring to other closely related species. Bolton (2007) and Wetterer (2008a) provide clarification of the actual species studied for many of the earlier publications on *T. albipes*.

Ants collected from south Florida in 1986 (Deyrup 1991) and identified as *T. albipes* were actually *Technomyrmex difficilis* (Bolton 2007). In the 1990s *T. difficilis* populations exploded to tremendous numbers in south and central Florida, overrunning landscapes and infesting structures (Hedges 1998b, Warner et al. 2005). These ants do not bite or sting, and have not been reported to cause structural damage (Warner 2003). However, their obvious foraging trails and ubiquitous presence around dwellings can create an aggravating nuisance to the public. Infestations have continued to spread in Florida, and isolated infestations (of presumably *T. difficilis*) have been reported from Georgia, North and South Carolina, and Louisiana (Warner et al. 2005; Warner and Scheffrahn 2005). *T. difficilis* infestations have also been confirmed in five West Indian islands (Wetterer 2008a). Isolated populations in California and large populations in Hawaii of supposedly white-footed ants have been identified as *Technomyrmex vitiensis* (Bolton 2007; Wetterer 2008a). Their presence in cut flowers from Hawaii can hinder export shipments, due to quarantine regulations (Hata et al. 1992). Because of the taxonomic confusion, extension and research publications for *T. albipes* in Florida are actually for *T. difficilis*, and these publications often cite *T. albipes* publications from Japan. These Japanese publications actually report on another related species, *Technomyrmex brunneus* Forel, instead of *T. albipes* (Bolton 2007).

IDENTIFICATION AND BIOLOGY

Distinguishing the several species previously identified as *T. albipes* requires specialized training and experience. General characteristics of the white-footed ants in the United States (i.e., *T. difficilis* and *T. vitiensis*) are as follows. Workers are about 2.7 mm long, dark brown to black in color, with pale-yellow lower legs (fig. 4.14). They have a one-segmented petiole without a node. They resemble odorous house ants, *Tapinoma sessile*, and some species of crazy ants (*Paratrechina* spp.), but white-footed ants have a granulate or microreticulate (fine netlike sculpturing) mesonotum and propodeum (Deyrup 1991; Vail et al. 1994). When observed from above, five gastral tergites are visible in the white-footed ants whereas only four gastral tergites are seen in the odorous house ant and other species of *Tapinoma* (Bolton 2007).

Based on the observations of *T. difficilis* in Florida and a similar species of white-footed

FIGURE 4.13.

White-footed ants entering a light switch. *Photo:* Fred Santana.

ants in Japan, *T. brunneus* (misidentified as *T. albipes* [Bolton 2007]), white-footed ants have decentralized colonies composed of many satellite nests extended over a large territory. A regular exchange of workers, brood, and food takes place between the nests. Colonies can have several million workers and numerous reproductive females (Yamauchi et al. 1991). A majority of the reproducing females are intercastes, which have characteristics of both queens and workers, including winglessness and having fewer ocelli, or simple eyes (Warner 2003). The presence of intercastes, as well as wingless males, represents a unique reproductive system among ants. The more typical mating flights by winged queens and males also occur, usually in July and August in south Florida (Warner et al. 2005).

White-footed ants often have nests in trees, sometimes located under loose bark and palm bracts, but are just as likely to be found nesting in soil at the base of trees and in leaf litter (Hedges 1998b; Warner 2003). They also nest in structures including wall voids, attics, and rain gutters; however, nesting sites tend to be outside of structures (Warner et al. 2005). *T. difficilis* tend hemipterans for honeydew and feed on plant nectar. They also feed on dead insects and other sources of protein. According to studies in Japan with *T. brunneus* (reported as *T. albipes*), colony members were fed with trophic eggs (i.e., sterile eggs used for food) and not by trophallaxis

(Yamauchi et al. 1991). However, in Florida, Warner (2003) reported behavior consistent with trophallaxis, and never observed feeding with trophic eggs. These contrasting observations may be indicative of the different ant species in Japan and Florida.

MANAGEMENT

Field and laboratory bioassays of various baits and residual sprays against *T. difficilis* in Florida indicated that liquid baits with carbohydrate or sweet attractant combined with a slow-acting toxicant were most efficacious in reducing test populations (Warner and Scheffrahn 2005). Residual insecticide sprays and baits have been used to suppress populations and trailing activity around structures. Due to large, mobile populations, control is often temporary as new colonies reinfest treated sites from surrounding areas. Managing structural infestations of white-footed ants often requires a combination of approaches and persistence. Reduce access to buildings by pruning trees and shrubs to eliminate any vegetation contact with walls and roofs, including falling leaves and branches that may harbor nests. Controlling aphid and scale insects in vegetation near structures may help reduce honeydew, a primary nutrient source for the ants, as well as a competing food source of baits (Warner et al. 2005). Dispensing sweet liquid ant baits along ant trails and replenishing baits frequently to maintain freshness will help reduce white-footed ant populations. Large, accessible colonies can also be treated directly with residual contact insecticides (Hedges 1998b).

GHOST ANTS

PEST STATUS

Ghost ants, *Tapinoma melanocephalum*, are a nuisance species found both indoors and outdoors throughout the tropics and subtropics worldwide. There also are scattered reports of infestations from temperate regions, primarily indoors in heated structures (Wetterer 2008b). In the United States ghost ants are well established in Florida and Hawaii, and they have been recently collected on the grounds of a nursery in southern Mississippi (MacGown and Hill 2009). Ghost ants have occasionally been reported from California

FIGURE 4.14.

Technomyrmex difficilis, a white-footed ant species found in Florida. Note the pale-yellow lower legs. *Photo:* Rudi Scheffrahn.

(Hedges 1997), Oregon, Washington, and other states (Wetterer 2008b). They are a ubiquitous tramp species, easily transported in cargo. Ghost ants have been considered to be from Africa or the Orient (Smith 1965), but a recent review suggested origin in the Indo-Pacific region, where India, Southeast Asia, and the western Pacific have the most records of this species (Wetterer 2008b). They do not sting nor have a painful bite (Wetterer 2008b); however, they have the potential to carry pathogens and have been found frequently in hospitals in Columbia and Brazil (Ulloa-Chacón and Jaramillo 2003; Pantoja et al. 2009). In infested buildings, ghost ants can be seen foraging across tabletops, trailing along baseboards and moldings, and then scurrying erratically when disturbed. They can be serious pests in insectaries and nature exhibits by preying on beneficial insects and contaminating displays, but occasionally may be beneficial because they will consume arthropod pests (Cook et al. 1994; Osborne et al. 1995; Nickerson et al. 2008).

IDENTIFICATION AND BIOLOGY

Ghost ants have a unique coloration of a very pale-whitish gaster and legs with a very dark brown to black head and mesosoma. The workers are very small, 1.3 to 1.5 mm long (fig. 4.15), and will quickly scurry in all directions when disturbed. Their small size and quick movements, combined with the difficulty of seeing their pale gaster, make them resemble tiny spiders (Vail et al. 1994). They have a one-segmented petiole that is flattened and does not have a conspicuous node. When viewing a ghost ant from the top, the petiole is hidden from view by an overhanging segment of the gaster. When crushed, ghost ants have a distinctively pungent *Tapinoma* odor, which resembles rotten coconuts (Smith 1965).

Ghost ant colonies can be moderate to large in size (100 to 1,000 individuals) with numerous queens (Smith 1965; Harada 1990). Queens resemble workers but are noticeably larger with darker gasters (fig. 4.16). New colonies are established by budding, and workers move freely between the nests along odor trails. It is not known whether they have mating flights (Harada 1990). Ghost ants nest in humid habitats as they are susceptible to desiccation (Appel et al. 2004). Nests are found in soil, rotten wood, under bark, and in plant cavities and detritus. In Florida, they are commonly found nesting at the base of palm fronds in decaying organic matter (Vail et al. 1994). Inside buildings, they nest in potted plants, breadboxes, shower curtain rods, inside irons, behind baseboards, in boxes inside infrequently used drawers or cabinets, between cabinets, and in other protected, dark harborages (Hedges 1997). Colonies also can relocate quickly among these numerous harborages, (DHO personal observations). Ghost ants commonly forage indoors from nesting sites located on the exterior of buildings. For

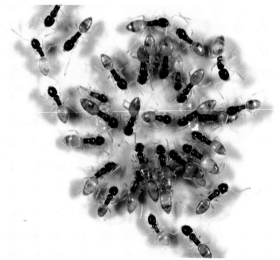

FIGURE 4.15.

Ghost ant workers. Note dark head and mesosoma and pale gaster. *Photo:* Reiner Pospischil.

FIGURE 4.16.

Ghost ant workers, queen, winged reproductive, and brood. *Photo:* Reiner Pospischil.

example, nests can be located in soil, trees, and shrubs next to foundations, in porches, and even in the hollow framing of pool enclosures. They gain access on vegetation touching the building, and enter cracks around windows, doors, and soffits (Vail et al. 1994; Hedges 1997).

Ghost ants tend hemipterans for honeydew and feed on both live and dead insects (Smith 1965). They can be voracious arthropod predators and have been observed to reduce spider mite populations and even insect cultures in greenhouses and insectaries (Osborne et al. 1995; DHO personal observation). In residences, their foraging activity is typically concentrated in the kitchen, where they commonly feed on sugar and other sweet foods like syrup, cakes, and candy. Less frequently, they can be seen foraging on grease deposits and other foods (Smith 1965; Hedges 1997).

MANAGEMENT

The difficulty of locating accessible ghost ant nests dictates the use of ant baits. Fire ant baits that use oil as an attractant are not normally foraged upon by ghost ants and thus are not effective. Bait preference tests using sugar attractants have indicated greater foraging on liquid and gel formulations over drier pastes used in containerized baits and granular particles (Lee 2008). Liquid ant baits containing boric acid or fipronil have killed small laboratory colonies when there was continuous access to fresh bait (Klotz et al. 1996; Ulloa-Chacón and Jaramillo 2003). Other commercially available liquid or gel

ant bait formulations with a carbohydrate-based attractant (sweet) and different active ingredients may also be effective in reducing ghost ant populations. Baits should be applied to locations where ants will encounter and forage on them, and preferably in sites protected from direct sunlight or rain to maintain bait freshness and acceptance by the ants. Baiting should be combined with other control measures, including sanitation, removing nesting sites and competing food sources, and pruning vegetation from buildings to minimize access from outdoor nests. Applications of nonrepellent residual insecticides to exterior walls along building foundations where ghost ants were trailing or nesting have been associated with less ghost ant foraging indoors (DHO personal observations).

PYRAMID ANTS

There are at least four species of *Dorymyrmex* in California: *D. insanus*, *D. bicolor*, *D. flavus*, and one undescribed species. *D. insanus* is often referred to as *D. pyramicus*, a species from South America, in some of the older literature. These ants often have cone-shaped piles of earth surrounding their nest entrances.

DORYMYRMEX INSANUS

PEST STATUS

The range of *D. insanus* extends east from Washington to New York and south to California and Florida (Smith 1965). It is extremely common in open native vegetation. It is reported as a structural infesting pest (Smith 1965). In the western United States it is not found in urban settings as often as *D. bicolor*; however, it is a common species in urban areas of Los Alamos, New Mexico (MacKay 1993).

IDENTIFICATION AND BIOLOGY

The workers are monomorphic, about 1.5 to 2 mm long, and uniformly brown. They have one node on the petiole. When crushed, they have a strong butyric acid or rotten coconut odor. The sharply conical protuberance on the posterior surface of the propodeum is also distinctive (fig. 4.17).

FIGURE 4.17.

Dorymyrmex insanus worker. Note the conical projection on the posterior surface of the propodeum. *Photo:* Courtesy of UC IPM.

D. insanus dominates desert grassland areas. The colonies are polydomous, occupying several square meters (Nickerson et al. 1975). Multiple queens are located in a central nest. In Southern California, single queen nests have been reported (Berkelhamer 1984). There is a lot of traffic between nests, transfer of brood, and food exchange (Buren et al. 1975).

This species is sometimes referred to as the *lion ant* because of its aggressive habits (Smith 1965). It scavenges on dead animals, but is also an active predator of insects. Workers will tend hemipterans producing honeydew. The presence of other insects and ants such as *Solenopsis invicta*, *Crematogaster ashmeadi*, and *Monomorium minimum* in their refuse piles attests to their aggressiveness (Hung 1974). However, colonies are able to coexist with a number of native *Formica* and *Pheidole* species (MacKay 1993).

MANAGEMENT

A corncob, grit-based, scatter bait with 0.045 percent indoxacarb, developed for fire ant control, provided about a 95 percent reduction in *D. insanus* within 1 day (Furman and Gold 2006). The numbers of ants increased between days 21 and 42.

DORYMYRMEX BICOLOR

PEST STATUS

The range of *D. bicolor* extends from Texas west to California and south to Mexico. Bicolored pyramid ants are more frequently collected by PMPs than other species of *Dorymyrmex*. Bicolored pyramid ants were collected in about 2 percent of the collections by PMPs in the Central Valley and lower deserts of California (Knight and Rust 1990). They were not commonly collected by PMPs in urban areas of San Diego (0.3%), but they were more common in Phoenix and Tucson, making up about 7 to 12 percent of the collections (Field et al. 2007).

The bicolored pyramid ant is extremely aggressive and has the potential to attack small, ground-nesting seabirds in coastal areas near San Diego.

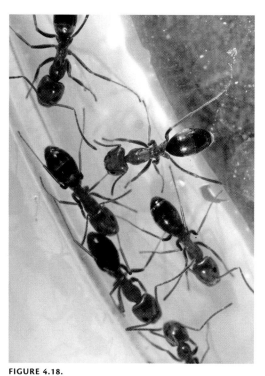

FIGURE 4.18.

Workers of *Dorymyrmex bicolor*. *Photo:* Courtesy of UC IPM.

IDENTIFICATION AND BIOLOGY

D. bicolor nest in open, dry, sunny areas (Klotz et al. 2008). The colonies are polydomous and polygynous, and workers (fig. 4.18) from different nests are not aggressive towards each other (Möglich and Alpert 1979). Nests contain multiple queens, from three to seven per colony (Berkelhamer 1984). The peak foraging period in coastal California is about 2 to 4 hours before sunset.

Bicolored ants have an interesting behavior when competing with other ants in their vicinity. The ants will drop small stones and other objects into the nest entrance of other species nesting near them (Möglich and Alpert 1979).

MANAGEMENT

This species does not readily accept most of the commercial ant baits available.

FORELIUS

Species belonging to the genus *Forelius* are considered to be dominant ants, based on their habitat requirements and competitive interactions (Andersen 1997). They are

FIGURE 4.19.

Forelius pruinosus workers feeding on sugar water. *Photo:* Dong-Hwan Choe.

extremely abundant, highly active, aggressive, and strong competitors of other ants. Two species are found in California, *Forelius pruinosus* (fig. 4.19) and *Forelius mccooki*. Both species have been collected by PMPs around structures (Knight and Rust 1990). However, very little is known about the biology of *F. mccooki*.

PEST STATUS

Forelius pruinosus is native to North America, ranging east from Wisconsin to New York and south to California, the Gulf Coast, and Florida (Smith 1965). It infests houses, particularly in the Gulf Coast states, and may nest indoors (Vail et al. 1994). In Phoenix and Tuscon, Arizona, it made up 18 and 15 percent, respectively, of the ants collected on service calls by PMPs (Field et al. 2007). It was primarily found outdoors. In California, it was found by PMPs around structures along the coastal region from Santa Barbara to Carlsbad in about 1.3 percent of the collections (Knight and Rust 1990).

IDENTIFICATION AND BIOLOGY

The body color of *F. pruinosus* is highly variable, ranging from dark brown to blackish in the eastern United States to a light brown in the western part of the country. This species has one node on the petiole and is frequently mistaken for Argentine ants in the western United States. The presence of pilosity on the middle dorsal thoracic segment helps distinguish this genus from *Linepithema* (Argentine ants). The presence of large and small teeth but no fine denticles on the worker mandibles of *Forelius* contrasts with the two large apical teeth and fine denticles on the workers' mandibles of *Linepithema* (Klotz et al. 2008). Freshly crushed workers have a rotten coconut odor similar to that of odorous house ants. *Forelius mccooki* has standing hairs on the scape, posterior margin of the head, and external face of tibiae that help differentiate it from *F. pruinosus* (Ward 2005).

F. pruinosus nests in open, grassy, or meadow areas under stones, logs, and other objects. It was one of the most commonly collected species on the North Carolina State University campus, especially along sidewalks and brick walkways (Nuhn and Wright 1979). They build a crater around the nest opening (Smith 1965). Like the Argentine ant, the colonies are polygynous and polydomous (Ward 2005; Hölldobler 1982). Unlike Argentine ants, swarms of adult males and females appear from May into July (Smith 1965).

Workers are diurnal, tending honeydew-producing hemipterans and collecting nectar from flowers. However, the ants are predaceous on other insects, especially termites and caterpillars (Rudgers et al. 2003). Workers dissect the prey and carry single fragments to their nest (Hölldobler 1962). *F. pruinosus* is capable of coexisting with red imported fire ants in native grasslands (Helms and Vinson 2001).

MANAGEMENT

Like most other dolichoderine ants, *F. pruinosus* is not attracted to oil-based baits (Valone and Kaspari 2005). The nest entrances can be drenched with insecticide (Hedges 1998a).

HARVESTER ANTS

PEST STATUS

Harvester ants play a critical role as granivores in desert ecosystems in the southwestern United States, along with rodents, birds, and other insects (Davidson et al. 1980). Two genera of harvester ants, *Pogonomyrmex* and *Messor*, are common in arid regions of California. As pests, the most significant impact of *Pogonomyrmex* is in agriculture, where they may cause damage to crops, rangelands, and livestock (Taber 1998). In urban environments they can become pests when homes are located in infested areas. And although they rarely invade homes, they are occasional pests in lawns, playgrounds, parks, and athletic fields because of the severe sting they may

inflict when their nest is disturbed (Ebeling 1975). Certain species of *Pogonomyrmex* also create large, circular, nest clearings, denuding vegetation and contributing to erosion. Although unable to sting, some species of *Messor* also create nests in yards, which homeowners may find objectionable (Ebeling 1975).

IDENTIFICATION AND BIOLOGY

There are about 2 dozen species of *Pogonomyrmex* in North America, most commonly found in the arid grasslands and deserts of the western United States. The genus name, *Pogonomyrmex*, means "bearded ant" in reference to the psammophore, a structure consisting of four fringes of long hairs on the posterior surface of the head behind the mouthparts on most but not all species (Taber 1998). The workers use this structure to carry seeds while foraging or sand during nest excavation (Wheeler and Wheeler 1986). Species vary in color from red to brown to black, as in the case of the light rusty red *P. californicus* (fig. 4.20) and the usually dark brownish black *P. rugosus* (fig. 4.21) (Ebeling 1975). All species have two nodes on the petiole. Workers of *P. rugosus* will often run excitedly with their gaster tucked forward under the thorax (Snelling and George 1979).

Messor species may be confused with *Pogonomyrmex*; however, the mesosomal profile

FIGURE 4.20.
Harvester ant worker, *Pogonomyrmex californicus*.
Photo: Gary Alpert.

FIGURE 4.21.

Harvester ant workers, *Pogonomyrmex rugosus*. *Photo:* Dong-Hwan Choe.

FIGURE 4.22.

Jet-black harvester ant worker, *Messor pergandei*. *Photo:* Courtesy of UC IPM.

of the latter is evenly convex (unlike the uneven profile of *Messor*), due to their distinctly depressed propodeum (Fisher and Cover 2007). Species of *Messor* are predominantly black, as in the case of the "jet-black, patent-leather-colored" *M. pergandei* (fig. 4.22) (Ebeling 1975). Along with their dark color, workers are polymorphic and possess a psammophore (Snelling and George 1979).

As the common name *harvester* implies, these ants collect seeds, which make up a major portion of their diet. Additionally, they feed on arthropods, and sometimes live prey in the case of *P. californicus.* The foraging behavior ranges from individual foraging in *P. californicus* to the long foraging columns of *M. pergandei.* On the other hand, *P. rugosus* exhibits both individual and column foraging depending on the density of seeds that are available (Snelling and George 1979).

Nests of *P. californicus* and *M. pergandei* are usually located in exposed areas, with both species forming craters in contrast to the flattened discs or low mounds that are characteristic of *P. rugosus* (Snelling and George 1979). Colonies of *M. pergandei* can be enormous (Fisher and Cover 2007), with some of the largest ant colonies of any North American species (Rissing 1988). Mating flights of *P. californicus* and *M. pergandei* occur in the spring while *P. rugosus* flights occur later in the summer during July and August (Snelling and George 1979).

MANAGEMENT

When elimination is warranted, a number of baits formulated with corn grit and soybean oil (imported fire ant baits) can be used effectively against harvester ants. For example, ant activity in nests of *P. californicus* and *P. rugosus* ceased within 48 hours and 2 to 3 weeks of treatment with these baits, respectively (Wagner 1983). When necessary, nests of *Messor* can be eliminated with an insecticide drench.

CRAZY ANTS

PEST STATUS

The crazy ant, *Paratrechina longicornis* (fig. 4.23), is a tramp and invasive species that has been widely distributed by commerce (Snelling and George 1979). It is believed to have originated in Asia or Africa and quickly spread throughout the world, often intercepted in plant quarantine (McGlynn 1999; Morgan et al. 2005). It is well established in many cities in the United States and has a significant presence in the Gulf Coast region (Smith 1965). In northern regions their occurrence is sporadic and typically found in apartment buildings, hotels, and greenhouses where they can be year-round pests (Smith 1965). They were the most common ants found in inspections of food processing plants in south Texas, and made up 14 percent of the pest ants collected by PMPs in a Florida survey (Shetlar and Walter 1982; Klotz et al.1995). In California, structural infestations have been reported in a hotel kitchen in San Francisco and occasional sightings have been reported in Southern California (Snelling and George 1979), such as, for example, sporadic infestations in the Los Angeles Basin. Another species, *P. vividula*, is common in many urban locations in California (Ward 2005), and Wheeler and Wheeler (1986) collected them at 16 sites in Nevada that were all associated with man-made structures.

IDENTIFICATION AND BIOLOGY

Workers of *P. longicornis* are small, slender, fast-moving ants with long legs and antennae and a dark brown to black body with bluish iridescence (Smith 1965; Snelling and George 1979). *P. vividula* is shiny in appearance, with a brown head, dark yellowish brown thorax, and dark brown gaster (Wheeler and Wheeler 1986). The common name, *crazy ant*, is derived from the characteristic jerky and erratic movements of *P. longicornis* (Thompson 1990).

As exotic pests, the biology of crazy ants is similar to that of Argentine ants. Both share several characteristics commonly associated with tramp or invasive ant species: unicolonial (supercolony), polygynous (multiple queens), and polydomous (multiple nests).

While typically ground dwelling, these pests can also be found nesting in homes and greenhouses (Creighton 1950) as well as in trash, cavities of trees, and rotten wood. Their colony size varies. For example, Blake (1940) found that most colonies were small, with approximately 2,000 workers and 8 to 40 queens, while Hedges (1997) found colonies numbering tens of thousands in Texas and Florida. It is not uncommon for colonies to move to new nesting sites (Blake 1940).

Crazy ants are omnivorous, feeding on honeydew and both live and dead insects (Smith 1965). *P. longicornis* became the predominant ant species in Biosphere 2 and

FIGURE 4.23.
Crazy ant worker, *Paratrechina longicornis*, carrying brood. *Photo:* Eric Paysen.

FIGURE 4.24.

False honey ant worker, *Prenolepis imparis*. *Photo:* Eric Paysen.

fed primarily on honeydew produced by mealybugs and scales (Wetterer et al. 1999). Also known as *sugar ants* because they have a preference for sweets, crazy ants will feed on various household foods.

MANAGEMENT

Inspections for crazy ant nests outdoors should focus especially on any piles of items in damp, shaded areas as well as in or under any objects lying on the ground such as trash, lumber, or stones (Hedges 1998a). Indoors, nests are sometimes located in wall voids and potted plants, and foragers are found along baseboards, both above and below carpeting (Hedges 1998a).

Nonchemical control measures include good housekeeping practices: removing potential food sources, cutting back shrubs and trees touching the structure, the use of weather-stripping around doors and windows, and caulking areas where ant intrusion is possible.

The Cooperative Extension Service in Florida, where crazy ants are major household pests, recommends sugar-based baits in the spring and fall, and protein-based baits in summer (Nickerson and Barbara 2000). Liquid baiting is more effective during the dry season as ants will attempt to gain access into the structure for water.

The best chemical control measure for crazy ants is the application of a slow-acting, residual perimeter insecticide. A thorough perimeter treatment, combined with direct applications to nests found on the property, is most effective (Hedges 1998a). Once an infestation has been established indoors, the use of baits and dusts in wall voids is most effective; however, these ants are often difficult to control, so persistence is critical.

WINTER, SMALL, OR FALSE HONEY ANT

PEST STATUS

The false honey ant, *Prenolepis imparis* (fig. 4.24), is found throughout the United States, sporadically in southern Canada, and in central Mexico, often associated with oak trees (Gregg 1963; Ebeling 1975; Wheeler and Wheeler 1986). It is common in California and often replaces the Argentine ant where the latter has been eliminated. When the ants are found in structures, they have usually come from outdoors. As pests, false honey ants commonly invade homes to forage and occasionally nest, as evidenced by alates sometimes found indoors (Smith 1965). Nesting under foundations has also been noted (Wegner 1991).

IDENTIFICATION AND BIOLOGY

As one of its common names suggests, the *winter ant* is cryophilic and begins foraging at temperatures around freezing (Talbot 1943; Creighton 1950). During the summer, these ants estivate or go through a "summer sleep" during which they forage very little or not at all (Talbot 1943). Mating flights take place early in spring, usually from March to April (Smith 1965). In Florida, their seasonal activity is restricted to November to April, and most colonies are polygynous (multiple queens) and contain 600 to 10,300 workers (Tschinkel 1987). Farther north, monogynous colonies that rarely exceed a few thousand individuals are more common (Smith 1965).

This ant typically constructs a crater nest in moist clay or loamy soils in well-shaded locations but seldom under stones or other objects (Smith 1965). Workers forage on live and dead insects (fig. 4.25), the juices of well-ripened or decaying fruits, the sap or juice from extracted flower buds, and the tender growth of certain plants (Smith 1965). Plants in contact with structures offer ants access, as do openings in plaster and stucco.

MANAGEMENT

Sweet baits, either liquid or gel, are readily taken by false honey ants (Wegner 1991, pers. comm. 2009). Homeowners, however, must follow good sanitation practices such as cleaning up food debris and beverage spills, because these will compete with the baits. Dust

FIGURE 4.25.

Foraging worker of *P. imparis* carrying insect. *Photo:* Gary Alpert.

FIGURE 4.26.

Moisture ants, *Lasius pallitarsis*, with brood. *Photo:* Laurel Hansen.

formulations of boric acid or diatomaceous earth are effective for treating nests in voids, and an application of fipronil on the outside foundation of the structure is also an effective control measure for this pest ant (Wegner 1991, pers. comm. 2009).

MOISTURE ANTS

PEST STATUS

Moisture ants are also known as *cornfield ants* because of the behavior of one species that tends aphids on corn plants. Most homeowners will not encounter this species but may have problems with other species of *Lasius*. The species that are associated with structures and moisture include other common names such as the *citronella ant*, the *black garden ant*, the *smaller yellow ant*, and the *larger yellow ant* (also called the *perfumed ant*). This large group of ants has been divided into five subgenera with 11 species in North America and 10 species in the western United States (Klotz et al. 2008). Nine of these species occur in California (Ward 2005). This discussion will be limited to two common groups (subgenera) found in the western United States: *Lasius* (moisture ants, fig. 4.26) and *Acanthomyops* (citronella ants). One of the unifying themes for this group is that they all nest in rotting logs and stumps or soil around rotting wood. Nests may also be found under stones. These ants are most often found in forested areas or in heavily landscaped areas. Ants will also nest in faulty woodwork or masonry of the basement or lower parts of a structure, particularly when wood is in contact with soil. Ants are capable of bringing moisture into a wood structure if conditions pre-existed for infestation (Akre and Antonelli 1992). Some species produce a carton material from soil, decayed wood, and water to create a nest.

IDENTIFICATION AND BIOLOGY

Most *Lasius* spp. (Subgenus *Lasius*) are monomorphic, about 2 to 3 mm long, and yellow to dark brown. They have one node on the petiole. The antennae are 12 segmented without a club. *Lasius* (Subgenus *Acanthomyops* spp.) are yellow and larger, with sizes varying from 3 to 5 mm. These ants may be confused with carpenter ants but can be distinguished

FIGURE 4.27.

Colony of acrobat ants. *Photo:* Alex Wild.

by a notch in the thoracic dorsum. They can be distinguished from thatching ants because they are generally smaller in size, monomorphic, and possess a rounded propodeal spiracle as opposed to the narrow slit-like propodeal spiracle on the thatching ants (Klotz et al. 2008). Winged males and females occur in nests in August through October, and the emergence of these winged forms may be the first indication of an infestation. Populations can be large and multi-queened. This group forages chiefly at night on honeydew, plus small live and dead insects (Smith 1965).

MANAGEMENT

Moisture ants are not considered a primary structural pest, but because they transport water into wooden structures that have contact with soil, they can increase the deterioration of wood (Akre and Antonelli 1992). The winged forms can become a nuisance in the fall when they swarm inside structures. Workers may also invade structures in search of food and moisture during summer months. Ants may also infest damaged wood in bathrooms that have moisture problems, especially when there is access through a crawlspace and plumbing lines. Evidence can include the dark-colored sawdust that may be excavated as nests are enlarged.

Inspection of structural perimeters should be made to identify and eliminate any wood in contact with soil. This also applies to any wet and decaying wood created by moisture or drainage problems such as leaking gutters, plumbing, improperly caulked windows, etc. Management includes the replacement of damaged wood with sound wood and the correction of problems causing wood decay. Chemical control will provide only a temporary solution by killing the foraging ants, but correction of moisture problems is required for complete control.

ACROBAT ANTS

PEST STATUS

Acrobat ants, *Crematogaster* spp., (fig. 4.27) are native throughout the western and southern states (Ebeling 1975) and are common in the Southwest including Southern California. The shape of the gaster and its petiolar attachment characterizes the species included in this group. Some species will nest in woodwork of houses, in rafters, shingles, and posts. They are also attracted to electrical wires and can cause short circuits by removing rubber insulation. Although the sting is vestigial, the ants will bite fiercely and will release a repulsive odor (Smith 1965). The most

FIGURE 4.28.

Worker of *Crematogaster coarctata*, very similar in appearance to *C. californica*. Photo: Alex Wild.

common species in California is *Crematogaster californica*, found in Southern California, with nests in soil or in decaying roots of desert plants (Snelling and George 1979). Other species of acrobat ants nest in dead branches of trees, other plants, and rotten logs, or they manufacture a carton for nest structure (Wheeler and Wheeler 1986).

IDENTIFICATION AND BIOLOGY

Acrobat ants are small or medium-sized ants (2.5 to 4 mm long) that vary in color from black to brown to reddish-yellow (fig. 4.28). The antenna is 11 segmented with a 3-segmented club. The mesosoma possesses two large spines directed posteriorly. The petiole has two nodes and is attached to the dorsal surface of the gaster. From above, the gaster appears heart-shaped. The dorsal surface of the gaster is rather flat while the ventral surface is strongly convex. When the ant is disturbed, the gaster is held above the mesosoma.

Acrobat ants forage on honeydew-producing insects as well as on other live and dead insects.

Within structures, acrobat ants will infest household foods with a preference for sweets and meats (Smith 1965).

Colonies can be quite large and have multiple queens (Fisher and Cover 2007). Winged forms are produced from mid-May to September (Hedges 1998a).

MANAGEMENT

Eliminating vegetation in contact with the building and correcting any moisture problems within the structure will eliminate the foraging opportunities and nesting sites of acrobat ants. When nests are located in a wall void, it may be necessary to inject a dust formulation of borate, silica compounds, or an aerosol that is labeled for ants through a small opening made at the base of the void. A careful inspection of the exterior should be made to discover nests under rocks or other landscaping materials. Nests on the exterior can be treated by the direct application of a formulation labeled for ants.

APPENDIX A. MORPHOLOGICAL FEATURES USED IN ANT TAXONOMY

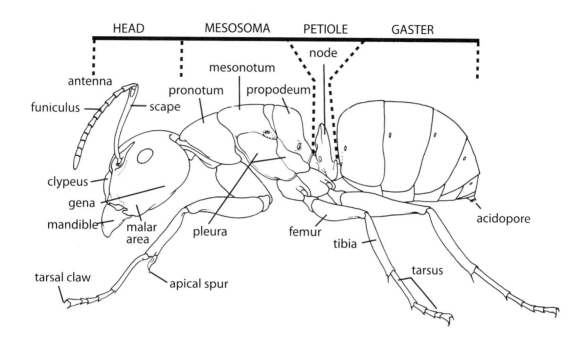

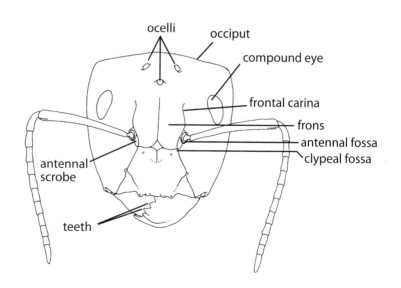

APPENDIX A

Illustrations: Janet Reynolds.
Source: Adapted from Hansen and Klotz 2005.

APPENDIX B

 # Key to Identifying Common Household Ants

This key includes nine of the most common ant species that are most likely to be a nuisance around California homes and structures. Many other ant species occur in California, but most are not home invaders.

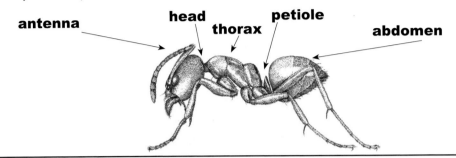

antenna   head   thorax   petiole   abdomen

One-node Ants

1A. Ant with one node on petiole (Fig. 1)
....*Go to step 2*
1B. Ant with two nodes on petiole (Fig. 2)
....*Go to step 5*

One node

Two nodes

(Fig.1)   (Fig. 2)

2A. Thorax is smooth and evenly rounded when viewed from the side (Fig. 3)
....*Go to step 3*
2B. Thorax is uneven in shape when viewed from the side (Fig. 4)
....*Go to step 4*

Thorax smooth and rounded

Thorax uneven in shape

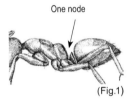 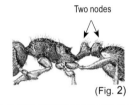

(Fig. 3)   (Fig. 4)

3A. Large, up to 1/2 inch long; black or reddish to dark brown; circle of hairs present on the tip of the abdomen (Fig. 5)
....*Carpenter ant*
3B. 1/8 to 1/4 inch long; brownish-black head, red thorax, and velvety black abdomen; no circle of hairs at tip of abdomen (Fig. 6)
....*Velvety tree ant*

Circle of hairs at tip of abdomen

No circle of hairs at tip of abdomen

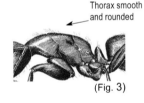 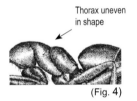

(Fig. 5 Carpenter ant)   (Fig. 6 Velvety tree ant)

4A. Node hidden by abdomen; dark brown to shiny-black in color; gives off a strong odor when crushed (Fig. 7)
....*Odorous house ant*
4B. Node erect; dull brown in color; gives off a musty odor when crushed (Fig. 8)
....*Argentine ant*

Node hidden by abdomen

Node erect

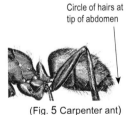 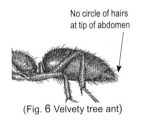

 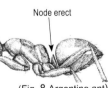

(Fig. 7 Odorous house ant)   (Fig. 8 Argentine ant)

Key to Identifying Common Household Ants (continued)
Two-node Ants

5A. One pair of spines on thorax (Fig. 9)
....**Pavement ant**

5B. No spines on thorax (Fig. 10)

....**Go to step 6**

One pair of spines

No spines on thorax

(Fig. 9 Pavement ant)   (Fig. 10)

6A. 12-segmented antenna ending with 3-segmented club (Fig. 11)

....**Pharaoh ant**

6B. 10-segmented antenna ending with 2-segmented club (Fig. 12)

....**Go to step 7**

3-segmented club

2-segmented club

(Fig. 11 Pharaoh ant)   (Fig. 12)

7A. Very small eyes; worker ants are all the same size, tiny, 1/32 inch long; yellow to light brown in color (Fig. 13)

....**Thief ant**

7B. Large eyes; worker ants are variable in size, 1/16 to 1/4 inch long; reddish to orange-brown in color with some black markings on the abdomen (Fig. 14)

....**Go to step 8**

Small eyes

Large eyes

(Fig. 13 Thief ant)   (Fig. 14)

8A. 3 small teeth on the front of the head; more prominent on larger workers (Fig. 15)

....**Red imported fire ant***

8B. 2 small teeth on the front of the head; more prominent on larger workers (Fig. 16)

....**Southern fire ant**

Three small teeth

Two small teeth

(Fig. 15 Red imported fire ant)*   (Fig. 16 Southern fire ant)

Argentine ant
(1/8 inch)

Carpenter ant
(1/4—1/2 inch)

Odorous house ant
(1/8 inch)

Pavement ant
(3/16 inch)

Pharaoh ant
(1/16 inch)

Red imported fire ant*
(1/16—1/5 inch)

Southern fire ant
(1/8—1/4 inch)

Thief ant
(1/32 inch)

Velvety tree ant
(1/8—1/4 inch)

*Red imported fire ant is not common and is an invading pest. Report suspected infestations to your county Agricultural Commissioner. For management information for other species, see the Ant Pest Note on the UC IPM Web site at www.ipm.ucdavis.edu.

(August 2005 Print copies of this key at www.ipm.ucdavis.edu/IDS/)   *Produced by the UC Statewide IPM Program*

GLOSSARY

active ingredient (AI). Toxic material used in baits, dusts, and sprays for insect management.

alate. A winged male or female reproductive, commonly called a *swarmer*.

ant bait. An insecticide formulation consisting of an active ingredient usually dissolved or suspended in a food that pest ant(s) will forage upon and feed to other colony members in the nest. (See **trophallaxis.**) The active ingredient should not kill ants immediately, but affect ants slowly to allow enough time for the bait to be distributed throughout the colony.

budding. Colony multiplication by fission in which one or more queens in the parent colony leave the nest along with some workers and brood to form a new colony.

cloaca. A common chamber containing the anus, genital duct or oviduct openings, and venom pore in ants.

cryophilic. A preference for lower temperatures.

dorsum. Referring to the uppermost surface of the body.

formic acid. Organic acid in venom of some ants, which acts as an alarm pheromone.

gaster. A globular-shaped section of the abdomen posterior to the petiole. (See drawing in appendix A.)

granivore. An herbivore that consumes grains or seeds.

hemiptera. A group of insects with sucking mouthparts that commonly feed on plants. Some hemipteran species produce honeydew (e.g., aphids, mealybugs, and scale insects).

honeydew. A liquid excrement produced by hemipterans containing sugars, amino acids, lipids, vitamins, and minerals.

insect growth regulator (IGR). A pesticide that disrupts normal development in insects through hormone or molting disruption.

integrated pest management (IPM). In structural pest control it refers to a systematic approach to managing pests that incorporates a number of elements, including habitat modification, sanitation, exclusion, and physical and chemical controls.

intercaste. An adult stage that has characteristics of both queens and workers.

major worker. The largest workers found within a polymorphic colony, often specialized for colony defense (see **soldier**) or other tasks such as cracking seeds.

mesonotum. The dorsal surface of the midthoracic segment. (See drawing in appendix A.)

mesosoma. The midsection of an ant, consisting of thorax and first abdominal segment. (See drawing in appendix A.)

minor worker. The smallest size of worker found within a polymorphic colony.

monogynous. Referring to one queen per colony.

monomorphic. Only one size of workers within a colony.

node. A dorsal projection of the petiole or postpetiole (see **petiole**) of various shapes but often resembling a knot or knob. On some species it is a flattened or scale-like projection on the petiole.

ocelli. Simple eyes found on some workers and on reproductives, which are located on the dorsum of the head. (See drawing in appendix A.)

omnivore. Consumes both plant-derived materials and animals.

pest management professional (PMP). Personnel licensed to manage structurally invading pests in urban environments using chemicals.

petiole. A narrow, constricted segment that forms a waist between the mesosoma and gaster of an ant. (See drawing in appendix A.) If there are two segments, the anterior—or first segment—is the petiole, and the second segment is the postpetiole.

pheromone. A glandular chemical secretion produced for some type of communication within a species.

photoperiod. The number of daylight hours in a 24-hour period.

pilosity. Body covering of fine, long hairs.

polydomous. Pertains to a colony with multiple nests as opposed to one central nest.

polygynous. Multiple queens coexisting within a single colony.

polymorphic. Having more than one size of workers within a colony.

propodeum. The first abdominal segment of an ant, which is fused to the thorax and is part of the mesosoma. (See drawing in appendix A)

psammophore. A fringe of long hairs on the posterior surface of the head behind the mouthparts.

satellite nest. The extension of a colony into a secondary nest(s) that may or may not contain a queen.

scape. The first antennal segment, which is normally the longest segment on adult workers and queens. (See drawing in appendix A.) Males sometimes have short scapes.

soldier. A worker found within a polymorphic colony that is specialized for colony defense, with an enlarged head and/or mandibles.

spiracles. The breathing pores found on the mesosoma and gaster (see drawing in appendix A) that open into the tracheal system (pulmonary system of insects).

sting. A modified ovipositor found in some ants that is associated with the venom gland.

supercolony. A unicolonial population consisting of many nests and queens that sometimes becomes enormous in size and spreads over large geographic areas. See **unicolonial**.

tergites. The dorsal or upper body surface of body segments.

trophallaxis. The liquid food exchange among colony members (e.g., oral trophallaxis), in which liquid food stored in the crop is regurgitated and shared with nestmates.

unicolonial. Relating to a colony with an open society characterized by individual ants moving freely between nests (nonterritorial) and lacking intraspecific aggression.

REFERENCES

Akre, R. D., L. D. Hansen, and E. A. Myhre. 1994. Colony size and polygyny in carpenter ants (Hymenoptera: Formicidae). Journal of the Kansas Entomological Society 67:1–9.

Akre, R. D., and A. L. Antonelli. 1992. Identification and habits of key ant pests of Washington (workers and winged reproductives). Washington State University Extension Bulletin EB0671.

Andersen, A. N. 1997. Functional groups and patterns of organization in North American ant communities: A comparison with Australia. Journal of Biogeography 24:433–460.

Appel, A. G., J. P.-S. Na, and C.-Y. Lee. 2004. Temperature and humidity tolerances of the ghost ant, *Tapinoma melanocephalum* (Hymenoptera: Formicidae). Sociobiology 44:89–100.

Aron, S. 2001. Reproductive strategy: An essential component in the success of incipient colonies of the invasive Argentine ant. Insectes Sociaux 48:25–27.

Bambara, S., M. Waldvogel, and J. Silverman. 2008. Argentine ants in the landscape and in the home. North Carolina State University Cooperative Extension Web site, http://www.ces.ncsu.edu/depts/ent/notes/O&T/trees/note140/note140.html.

Barbani, L. E. 2003. Foraging activity and food preferences of the odorous house ant (*Tapinoma sessile* Say) (Hymenoptera: Formicidae). MS Thesis. Virginia Tech.

Barbani, L., and R. Fell. 2002. How odorous house ants elude control. Pest Control 70(3): 20–22.

Barr, C. L., T. Davis, K. Flanders, W. Smith, L. Hooper-Bui, P. Koehler, K. Vail, W. Gardner, B. M. Drees, and T. W. Fuchs. 2005. Broadcast baits for fire ant control. Texas A&M Univ. System publication.

Barr, C. L., W. Summerlin, and B. M. Drees. 1999. A cost/efficacy comparison of individual mound treatments and broadcast baits. Proceedings of the Imported Fire Ant Conference. Charleston, South Carolina. 31–36.

Beatson, S. H. 1972. Pharaoh's ants as pathogen vectors in hospitals. Lancet 1:425–427.

_____. 1973. Pharaoh's ants entering giving-sets. Lancet 1:606.

Berkelhamer, R. C. 1984. An electrophoretic analysis of queen number in these species of dolichoderinae ants. Insectes Sociaux 31:132–141.

Blake, C. H. 1940a. Notes on economic ants. Pests 8(11): 16–18.

_____. 1940b. Notes on economic ants. Part II. Pests 8(12): 8–10.

Blum, M. S., and H. R. Hermann. 1978. Venoms and venom apparatuses of the Formicidae: Myrmeciinae, Ponerinae, Dorylinae, Pseudomyrmecinae, Myrmicinae, and Formicinae. In S. Bettini, ed., Arthropod venoms. Berlin: Springer Verlag. 801–869.

Bolton, B. 2007. Taxonomy of the dolichoderine ant genus *Technomyrmex* Mayr (Hymenoptera: Formicidae) based on the worker cast. Contributions of the American Entomological Institute 35:1–150.

Buczkowski, G., and G. Bennett. 2006. Dispersed central-place foraging in the polydomous odorous house ant, *Tapinoma sessile*, as revealed by a protein marker. Insectes Sociaux 53:282–290.

_____. 2008. Seasonal polydomy in a polygynous supercolony of the odorous house ant, *Tapinoma sessile*. Ecological Entomology 33:780–788.

Buczkowski, G., M. E. Scharf, C. R. Ratliff, and G. W. Bennett. 2005. Efficacy of simulated barrier treatments against laboratory colonies of Pharaoh ant. Journal of Economic Entomology 98:485–492.

Buren, W. F., J. C. Nickerson, and C. R. Thompson. 1975. Mixed nests of *Conomyrma insana* and *C. flavopecta*: Evidence of parasitism (Hymenoptera: Formicidae). Psyche 82(3–4): 306–314.

California Department of Pesticide Regulation (CDPR). 2009. Definition of IPM (integrated pest management). CDPR Web site, apps.cdpr.ca.gov/schoolipm/overview/definition_ipm.cfm.

Coarsey, J. M. 1952. Southern fire ant, *Solenopsis xyloni* (death of a child in Mississippi). Cooperative Economic Insect Report September 19, p. 301.

Cook, J. L., J. B. Martin, and R. E. Gold. 1994. First record of *Tapinoma melanocephalum* (Hymenoptera: Formicidae) in Texas. Southwestern Entomologist 19:409–410.

Creighton, W. S. 1950. The ants of North America. Bulletin of the Museum of Comparative Zoology at Harvard College: 104.

Davidson, D. W., J. H. Brown, and R. S. Inouye. 1980. Competition and the structure of granivore communities. BioScience 30:233–238.

Deyrup, M. 1991. *Technomyrmex albipes*, a new exotic ant in Florida (Hymenoptera: Formicidae). Florida Entomologist 74:147–148.

Deyrup, M., L. Davis, and S. Cover. 2000. Exotic ants in Florida. Transactions of the American Entomological Society 126:293–326.

Douglen, L. 2005. Carpenter ants eating US homes. Washington, D.C.: ExpertClick Broadcast Interview Source, Inc.

Drees, B. M., S. B. Vinson, R. E Gold, M. E. Merchant, E. Brown, K. Engler, M. Keck, P. Nester, D. Kostroun, K. Flanders, F. Graham, D. Pollet, L. Hooper-Bui, P. Beckley, T. Davis, O. M. Horton, W. Gardner, K. Loftin, K. Vail, R. Wright, W. Smith, D. C. Thompson, J. Kabashima, B. Layton, P. Koehler, D. Oi, and A-M. Callcott. 2006. Managing imported fire ants in urban areas; A regional publication developed for: Alabama, Arkansas, California, Florida, Georgia, Louisiana, Mississippi, New Mexico, Oklahoma, South Carolina, Tennessee and Texas. College Station, TX: Texas A&M University. Texas Cooperative Extension, B-6043.

Ebeling, W. 1975. Urban entomology. Berkeley: University of California Press.

Edwards, J. P. 1985. The development of methoprene baits for the control of the Pharaoh's ant, *Monomorium pharaonis*. Proceedings of the Insect Growth Regulator Symposium, Dallas, Texas. 25–31.

Edwards, J. P. 1986. The biology, economic importance, and control of the Pharaoh's ant, *Monomorium pharaonis* (L.). In S. B. Vinson, ed., Economic impact and control of social insects. New York: Praeger. 257–271.

Edwards, J. P., and L. Abraham. 1990. Changes in food selection by workers of the pharaoh's ant, *Monomorium pharaonis*. Medical and Veterinary Entomology 4:205–211.

Field, H. C., W. E. Evans, R. Hartley, L. D. Hansen, and J. H. Klotz. 2007. A survey of structural ant pests in the southwestern U.S.A. (Hymenoptera: Formicidae). Sociobiology 49:1–14.

Field, H. C., and J. H. Klotz. 2008. Who's better at Argentine ant control? Pest Control Technology 36(3): 76,78,80.

Fisher, B. L., and S. P. Cover. 2007. Ants of North America: A guide to the genera. Berkeley: University of California Press.

Flint, M. L. 2003. Residential pesticide use in California: A report of surveys taken in the Sacramento (Arcade Creek), Stockton (Five Mile Slough) and the San Francisco Bay Areas with comparisons to the San Diego Creek Watershed of Orange County, California. UC IPM Web site, www.ipm.ucdavis.edu/PDF/PUBS/ncalifsurvey_1.pdf.

Furman, B. D. and R. E Gold. 2006. The effectiveness of label-rate broadcast treatment with Advion at controlling multiple ant species (Hymenoptera: Formicidae). Sociobiology 48:559–570.

Goddard, J., J. Jarratt, and R. D. deShazo. 2002. Recommendations for prevention and management of fire ant infestation of health care facilities. Southern Medical Journal 95:627–633.

Gordon, D. M., L. Moses, M. Falkovitz-Halpern, and E. H. Wong. 2001. Effect of weather on infestation of buildings by the invasive Argentine ant, *Linepithema humile* (Hymenoptera: Formicidae). American Midland Naturalist Journal 146:321–328.

Greenberg, L., J. H. Klotz, and J .N. Kabashima. 2008. Red imported fire ant. UC IPM Pest Note. UC IPM Web site, http://www.ipm.ucdavis.edu/PMG/PESTNOTES/pn7487.html.

Greenberg, L., D. Reierson, and M. K. Rust. 2003. Fipronil trials in California against the red imported fire ant, *Solenopsis invicta* Buren, using sugar water consumption and mound counts as measures of ant abundance. Journal of Agriculture and Urban Entomology 20:221–233.

Greenberg, L., M. K. Rust, J. H. Klotz, D. Haver, J. N. Kabashima, S. Bondarenko, and J. Gan. 2010. Impact of ant control techniques on insecticide runoff and efficacy. Pest Management Science. In press.

Gregg, R. E. 1963. The ants of Colorado. Boulder: University of Colorado Press.

Gulmahamad, H. 1995. The genus *Liometopum* Mayr (Hymenoptera: Formicidae) in California, with notes on nest architecture and structural importance. Pan-Pacific Entomologist 71(2): 82–86.

Haack, K. D. 1991. Pharaoh ants, an analysis of field trials with Pro-Control and Maxforce ant baits. Pest Control Technology (19):32–33,36,38,42.

Hansen, L. D., and J. H. Klotz. 2005. Carpenter ants of the United States and Canada. Ithaca, NY: Cornell University Press.

Hansen, L. 2007. Panic! Carpenter ants during the dormant season. Pest Control Technology 35(4): 34,36–38.

Hansen, L. 2008. Not in my backyard. Pest Control Technology 36(4): 70,72,74–75.

Harada, A. Y. 1990. Ant pests of the Tapinomini tribe. In R. K. VanderMeer, K. Jaffe, and A. Cedeno, eds., Applied myrmecology: A world perspective. Boulder, Colorado: Westview Press. 298–309.

Hata, T. Y., A. H. Hara, E. B. Jang, L. S. Imaino, B. K. S. Hu, and V. L. Tenbrink. 1992. Pest management before harvest and insecticidal dip after harvest as a systems approach to quarantine security for red ginger. Journal of Economic Entomology 85:2310–2316.

Hedges, S. A. 1997. Ants. In D. Moreland, ed., Handbook of pest control. 8th ed. Mallis Handbook and Technical Training Company. 503–589.

———. 1998a. Field guide for the management of structure-infesting ants. 2nd ed. Cleveland, Ohio: Franzak and Foster.

———. 1998b. Another exotic ant on the prowl. Pest Control Technology 26(7): 56,58,60,62–63.

Helms, K. R., and S. B. Vinson. 2001. Coexistence of native ants with red imported fire ant, Solenopsis invicta. Southwestern Naturalist 46:396–400.

Hoffman, D. R. 1997. Reactions to less common species of fire ants. Journal of Allergy and Clinical Immunology 100:679–683.

Hölldobler, B. 1962. Interference strategy of Iridomyrmex pruinosum (Hymenoptera: Formicidae) during foraging. Oecologia 52:208–213.

Hölldobler, B., and E. O. Wilson. 1990. The ants. Cambridge, MA: Harvard University Press.

Hooper, L. M., M. K. Rust, and D. A. Reierson. 1998. Using bait to suppress the southern fire ant on an ecologically sensitive site (Hymenoptera: Formicidae). Sociobiology 31:283–289.

Hung, A. C. F. 1974. Ants recovered from refuse piles of the pyramid ant Conomyrma insana (Buckley) (Hymenoptera: Formicidae). Annals of the Entomological Society of America 67:522–523.

Kemp, S. F., R. D. deShazo, J. E. Moffitt, D. F. Williams, and W. A. Buhner. 2000. Expanding habitat of the imported fire ant (Solenopsis invicta): A public health concern. Journal of Allergy and Clinical Immunology 105:683–691.

King, J. R., and W. R. Tschinkel. 2008. Experimental evidence that human impacts drive fire ant invasions and ecological change. Proceedings of the National Academy of Sciences 105:20339–20343.

Klotz, J., and G. Bennett. 1992. Carpenter ants: The urban pest management challenge. Pest Control 60(5): 44–45,48,50.

Klotz, J. H., L. Greenberg, H. H. Shorey, and D. F. Williams. 1997. Alternative control strategies for ants around homes. Journal of Agricultural Entomology 14:249–257.

Klotz, J., L. Hansen, R. Pospischil, and M. Rust. 2008. Urban ants of North America and Europe. Ithaca, NY: Cornell University Press.

Klotz, J. H., J. R. Mangold, K. M. Vail, L. R. Davis, and R. S. Patterson. 1995. A survey of the urban pest ants (Hymenoptera: Formicidae) of peninsular Florida. Florida Entomologist 78:109–118.

Klotz, J. H., D. H. Oi, K. M. Vail, and D. F. Williams. 1996. Laboratory evaluation of a boric acid liquid bait on colonies of Tapinoma melanocephalum, Argentine ants, and Pharaoh ants (Hymenoptera: Formicidae). Journal of Economic Entomology 89:673–677.

Klotz, J. H., M. K. Rust, L. Greenberg, H. C. Field, and K. Kupfer. 2007. An evaluation of several urban pest management strategies to control Argentine ants (Hymenoptera: Formicidae). Sociobiology 50:1–8.

Klotz, J. H., M. K. Rust, H. C. Field, L. Greenberg, and K. Kupfer. 2009. Low impact directed sprays and liquid baits to control Argentine ants (Hymenoptera: Formicidae). Sociobiology 54:101–108.

Klotz, S. A., J. O. Schmidt, R. E. Kohlmeier, D. R. Suiter, J. L. Pinnas, and J. H. Klotz. 2004. Stinging ants: Case histories of three native North American species. In Proceedings, 2004 National Conference on Urban Entomology. 108–109.

Klotz, J. H., K. M. Vail, and D. F. Williams. 1997. A liquid boric acid bait used against structural infestations of Pharaoh ants (Hymenoptera: Formicidae). Journal of Economic Entomology 90:523–526.

Knight, R. L., and M. K. Rust. 1990. The urban ants of California with distribution notes of imported species. Southwestern Entomologist 15:167–178.

Lard, C. F., J. Schmidt, B. Morris, L. Estes, C. Ryan, and D. Bergquist. 2006. An economic impact of imported fire ants in the United States of America. College Station, Texas: Texas A&M University. Dr. Curtis F. Lard's Web site at TAMU's Department of Agricultural

Economics, http://fireantecon.tamu.edu/Publications/Copy percent20of percent20the percent20National percent20Study.pdf.

Lee, C. -Y. 2008. Sucrose bait base preference of selected urban pest ants (Hymenoptera: Formicidae). In W. H. Robinson and D. Bajomi, eds., Proceedings of the 6th International Conference Urban Pests, July 13–16, 2008, Budapest, Hungary. 59–63.

Lofgren, C. S. 1986. The economic importance and control of imported fire ants in the United States. In S. B. Vinson, ed., Economic impact and control of social insects. New York: Praeger Publishers. 227–256.

Lowe, S., M. Browne, S. Boudjelas, and M. De Poorter. 2000. 100 of the world's worst invasive alien species. A selection from the global invasive species database. The Invasive Species Specialist Group of the Species Survival Commission of the World Conservation Union.

MacGown J., and J. G. Hill. 2009. *Tapinoma melanocephalum* (Hymenoptera: Formicidae), a new exotic ant in Mississippi. Journal of the Mississippi Academy of the Sciences 54:172–174.

MacKay, W. P. 1993. Succession of ant species (Hymenoptera: Formicidae) on low-level nuclear waste sites in northern New Mexico. Sociobiology 23:1–11.

Macom, T. E., and S. D. Porter. 1996. Comparison of polygyne and monogyne red imported fire ant (Hymenoptera: Formicidae) population densities. Annals of the Entomological Society of America 89:535–543.

Mampe, D. 1993. Pharaoh bait knocks out pavement ants. Pest Control 61(3): 8.

McGlynn, T. P. 1999. The worldwide transfer of ants: Geographical distribution and ecological invasions. Journal of Biogeography 26:535–548.

Merchant, M., and B. M. Drees. 1992. The two-step method do-it-yourself fire ant control. Texas Agricultural Extension Service Leaflet L-5070.

Möglich, M. H. J., and G. D. Alpert. 1979. Stone dropping by *Conomyrma bicolor* (Hymenoptera: Formicidae): A new technique of interference competition. Behavioral Ecology and Sociobiology 6:105–113.

Morgan, E. D., B. D. Jackson, and J. Billen. 2005. Chemical secretions of the "crazy ant" *Paratrechina longicornis* (Hymenoptera: Formicidae). Sociobiology 46:299–304.

Newell, W., and T. C. Barber. 1913. The Argentine ant. USDA Bureau of Entomology Bulletin 122.

Newton, J. 1980. Alternatives to chlordecone for Pharaoh's ant control. International Pest Control 22:112–135.

Nickerson, J. C., and K. A. Barbara. 2000. Featured creatures: Crazy ant. University of Florida Institute of Food and Agricultural Sciences Web site, http://entnemdept.ufl.edu/creatures/.

Nickerson, J. C., C. L. Bloomcamp, and R. M. Pereira. 2008. Ghost ant, *Tapinoma melanocephalum* (Fabricius) (Insecta: Hymenoptera: Formicidae). University of Florida Institute of Food and Agricultural Sciences Extension, EENY-310. University of Florida IFAS Extension Web site, http://edis.ifas.ufl.edu/IN532.

Nickerson, J. C., H. L. Cromroy, W. H. Whitcomb, and J. A. Cornell. 1975. Colony organization and queen numbers in two species of *Conomyrma*. Annals of the Entomological Society of America 68:1083–1085.

Nuhn, T. P., and C. G. Wright. 1979. An ecological survey of ants (Hymenoptera: Formicididae) in a landscaped suburban habitat. American Midland Naturalist Journal 102:353–362.

Oi, F. M. 2005. Household ants still #1 pest. Florida Pest Pro Magazine 1:12,14,16.

Oi, D. H. 2008. Pharaoh ants and fire ants. In X. Bonnefoy, H. Kampen, and K. Sweeney, eds., Public health significance of urban pests. Copenhagen, Denmark: WHO Publications. 175–208.

Oi, D. H., and D. F. Williams. 1996. Toxicity and repellency of potting soil treated with bifenthrin and tefluthrin to red imported fire ants (Hymenoptera: Formicidae). Journal of Economic Entomology 89:1526–1530.

Oi, D. H., K. M. Vail, and D. F. Williams. 2000. Bait distribution among multiple colonies of Pharaoh ants (Hymenoptera: Formicidae). Journal of Economic Entomology 93:1247–1255.

Osborne, L. S., J. E. Peña, and D. H. Oi. 1995. Predation by *Tapinoma melanocephalum* (Hymenoptera: Formicidae) on twospotted spider mites (Acari: Tetranychidae) in Florida greenhouses. Florida Entomologist 78:565–570.

Pantoja, L. D. M., R. E. Moreira Filho, E. H. S. Brito, T. B. Aragão, R. S. N. Brilhante, R. A. Cordeiro, M. F. G. Rocha, A. J. Monteiro, Y. P. Quinet, and J. J. C. Sidrim. 2009. Ants (Hymenoptera: Formicidae) as carriers of fungi in hospital environments: An emphasis on the genera *Tapinoma* and *Pheidole*. Journal of Medical Entomology 46:895–899.

Passera, L. 1994. Characteristics of tramp species. In D. F. Williams, ed., Exotic ants: Biology, impact, and control of introduced species. Boulder, CO: Westview Press. 23–43.

Pinto, L. 1990. Several options for controlling pavement ants. Pest Control 58(9): 48,56.

Porter, S. D., and D. A. Savignano. 1990. Invasion of polygyne fire ants decimates ants and disrupts arthropod community. Ecology 71:2095–2106.

Reierson, D. A., M. K. Rust, and J. Hampton-Beesley. 1998. Monitoring with sugar water to determine the efficacy of treatments to control Argentine ants, Linepithema humile (Mayr). Proceedings of the 1998 National Conference on Urban Entomology. 78–82.

Rissing, S. W. 1988. Group foraging dynamics of the desert seed-harvester ant Veromessor pergandei (Mayr). In J. C. Trager, ed., Advances in myrmecology. New York: E. J. Brill. 347–353.

Rudgers, J. A., J. G. Hodgen, and J. W. White. 2003. Behavioral mechanisms underlie an ant-plant mutualism. Oecologia 135:51–59.

Rust, M. K., K. Haagsma, and D. A. Reierson. 1996. Barrier sprays to control Argentine ants (Hymenoptera: Formicidae). Journal of Economic Entomology 89:134–137.

Rust, M. K., D. A. Reierson, and J. H. Klotz. 2002. Factors affecting the performance of bait toxicants for Argentine ants (Hymenoptera: Formicidae). In S. C. Jones, J. Zhai, and W.H. Robinson, eds., Proceedings of the Fourth International Conference on Urban Pests. Blacksburg, VA: Pocahontas Press. 115–120.

_____. 2004. Delayed toxicity as a critical factor in the efficacy of aqueous baits for controlling Argentine ants (Hymenoptera: Formicidae). Journal of Economic Entomology 97:1017–1024.

Scharf, M. E., C. R. Ratliff, and G. W. Bennett. 2004. Impacts of residual insecticide barriers on perimeter-invading ants, with particular reference to the odorous house ant, Tapinoma sessile. Journal of Economic Entomology 97:601–605.

Schlick-Steiner, B. C., F. M. Steiner, K. Moder, B. Seifert, M. Sanetra, E. Dyreson, C. Stauffer, and E. Christian. 2006. A multidisciplinary approach reveals cryptic diversity in Western Palearctic Tetramorium ants (Hymenoptera: Formicidae). Molecular Phylogenetics and Evolution 40:259–273.

Shetlar, D. J., and V. E. Walter. 1982. Ants. In K. Story, ed., Mallis handbook of pest control. 6th ed. Cleveland, OH: Franzak and Foster. 424–487.

Silverman, J., and R. J. Brightwell. 2008. The Argentine ant: Challenges in managing an invasive unicolonial pest. Annual Review of Entomology 53:231–252.

Smith, M. R. 1965. House-infesting ants of the eastern United States: Their recognition, biology, and economic importance. Agricultural Research Service, USDA Technical Bulletin. No. 1326.

Snelling, R. R., and C. D. George. 1979. The taxonomy, distribution and ecology of California desert ants (Hymenoptera: Formicidae). Report to California Desert Plan Program. Washington, D.C.: Bureau of Land Management, U.S. Department of the Interior.

Soeprono, A. M., and M. K. Rust. 2004a. Effect of delayed toxicity of chemical barriers to control Argentine ants (Hymenoptera: Formicidae). Journal of Economic Entomology 97:2021–2028.

_____. 2004b. The effect of horizontal transfer of barrier insecticides to control Argentine ants (Hymenoptera: Formicidae). Journal of Economic Entomology 97:1675–1681.

Suarez, A. V., J. Q. Richmond, and T. J. Case. 2000. Prey selection in horned lizards following the invasion of Argentine ants in southern California. Ecological Applications 10:711–725.

Taber, S. W. 1998. The world of the harvester ant. College Station, TX: Texas A&M University Press.

Taber, S. W. 2000. Fire ants. College Station, TX: Texas A&M University Press.

Talbot, M. 1943. Responses of the ant Prenolepis imparis to temperature and humidity changes. Ecology 24:345–352.

Taniguchi, G., T. Thompson, and B. Sipes. 2005. Control of the big-headed ant, Pheidole megacephala (Hymenoptera: Formicidae), in pineapple cultivation using Amdro in bait stations. Sociobiology 45:1–7.

Thompson, C. R. 1990. Ants that have pest status in the United States. In R. K. Vander der Meer, K. Jaffe, and A. Cedeno, eds., Applied myrmecology: A world perspective. Boulder, CO: Westview Press. 51–67.

Tschinkel, W. R. 1987. Seasonal life history and nest architecture of a winter-active ant, Prenolepis imparis. Insectes Sociaux 34:143–164.

Ulloa-Chacón, P., and G. I. Jaramillo. 2003. Effects of boric acid, fipronil, hydramethylnon, and diflubenzuron baits on colonies of ghost ants (Hymenoptera: Formicidae). Journal of Economic Entomology 96:856–862.

Vail, K. M. 1997. Pharaoh ant control in large institutions: Or spraying is not for pharaoh ants. University of Tennessee Agricultural Extension Service Publication 623.

Vail, K. M., D. Bailey, and M. McGinnis. 2003. Perimeter spray and bait combo. Pest Control Technology 31:96–100.

Vail, K., L. Davis, D. Wojcik, P. Koehler, and D. Williams. 1994. Structure-invading ants of Florida. University of Florida, IFAS. SP 164.

Valone, T. J., and M. Kaspari. 2005. Interactions between granivorous and omnivorous ants in a desert grassland: Results from a long-term experiment. Ecological Entomology 30:116–121.

Varlamoff, S., W. J. Florkowski, J. L. Jordan, J. Latimer, and K. Braman. 2001. Georgia homeowner survey of landscape management practices. HortTechnology 11:326–331.

Vega, S. Y., and M. K. Rust. 2001. The Argentine ant: A significant invasive species in agriculture, urban and natural environments. Sociobiology 37:3–25.

Vega, S. J., and M. K. Rust. 2003. Determining the foraging range and origin of resurgence after treatment of Argentine ant (Hymenoptera: Formicidae) in urban areas. Journal of Economic Entomology 96:844–849.

Vinson, S. B. 1997. Invasion of the red imported fire ant (Hymenoptera: Formicidae): Spread, biology, and impact. American Entomologist 43:23–39.

Wagner, R. E. 1983. Effects of Amdro fire ant insecticide mound treatments on southern California ants. Insecticide & Acaracide Tests 8:257.

Ward, P. S. 2005. A synoptic review of the ants of California (Hymenoptera: Formicidae). Zootaxa 936:1–68.

Warner, J. R. 2003. Bait preferences and toxicity of insecticides to white-footed ants *Technomyrmex albipes* (Hymenoptera: Formicidae). M.S. thesis, University of Florida, Gainesville.

Warner, J., and R. H. Scheffrahn. 2005. Laboratory evaluation of baits, residual insecticides, and an ultrasonic device for control of white-footed ant, *Technomyrmex albipes* (Hymenoptera: Formicidae). Sociobiology 45:317–330.

Warner, J., R. H. Scheffrahn, and B. Cabrera. 2005. White-footed ant, *Technomyrmex albipes* (Fr. Smith) (Insecta: Hymenoptera: Formicidae: Dolichoderinae). University of Florida IFAS Extension. EENY-273.

Warner, J., and R. H. Scheffrahn. 2007. Bigheaded ant, *Pheidole megacephala* (Fabricius) (Insecta: Hymenoptera: Formicidae: Myrmicinae). University of Florida IFAS Extension. EENY-369.

Warner, J., and R.H. Scheffrahn. 2008. Efficacy of selected bait and residual toxicants for control of bigheaded ants, *Pheidole megacephala* (Hymenoptera: Formicidae), in large field plots. Florida Entomologist 91:277–282.

Wegner, G. 1991. The small honey ant. Pest Management 10:28–29.

Wetterer, J. K. 2008a. *Technomyrmex difficilis* (Hymenoptera: Formicidae) in the West Indies. Florida Entomologist 91:428–430.

_____. 2008b. Worldwide spread of the ghost ant, *Tapinoma melanocephalum* (Hymenoptera: Formicidae). Myrmecological News 12:23–33.

Wetterer, J. K., S. E. Miller, D. E. Wheeler, C. A. Olson, D. A. Polhemus, M. Pitts, I. W. Ashton, A. G. Himler, M. M. Yospin, K. R. Helms, E. L. Harken, J. Gallager, C. E. Dunning, M. Nelson, J. Litsinger, A. Southern, and T. L. Burgess. 1999. Ecological dominance by *Paratrechina longicornis* (Hymenoptera: Formicidae), an invasive tramp ant, in Biosphere 2. Florida Entomologist 82:381–388.

Wheeler, W. M. 1910. Ants. New York: Columbia University Press.

Wheeler, G. C., and J. N. Wheeler. 1986. The ants of Nevada. Los Angeles: Natural History Museum of Los Angeles County.

Williams, D. F., H. L. Collins, and D. H. Oi. 2001. The red imported fire ant (Hymenoptera: Formicidae): A historical perspective of treatment programs and the development of chemical baits for control. American Entomologist 47:146–159.

Wilson, E. O. 2003. *Pheidole* in the New World. Cambridge, MA: Harvard University Press.

Wright, C. G., and D. Stout. 1981. Boric acid bait update. Pest Control 49(5):15,75.

Yamauchi, K., T. Furukawa, K. Kinomura, H. Takamine, and K. Tsuji. 1991. Secondary polygyny by inbred wingless sexuals in the dolichoderine ant *Technomyrmex albipes*. Behavioral Ecology and Sociobiology 29:313–319.

MEASUREMENT CONVERSION TABLE

U.S. Customary	Conversion factor for U.S. Customary to metric	Conversion factor for metric to U.S. Customary	Metric
inch (in)	2.54	0.394	centimeter (cm)
foot (ft)	0.3048	3.28	meter (m)
acre (ac)	0.4047	2.47	hectare (ha)
gallon (gal)	3.785	0.26	liter (l)
ounce (oz)	28.35	0.035	gram (g)
pound (lb)	0.454	2.205	kilogram (kg)
pound per acre (lb/ac)	1.12	0.89	kilogram per hectare (kg/ha)

INDEX